THE SONGLESS AVIARY:
THE WORLD OF A. E. CROWELL & SON

A Loan Exhibition

May 10 through October 25, 1992

Heritage Plantation of Sandwich
Brian Cullity, Curator, Art Museum
with an essay by
Gigi Hopkins

Designed and Printed by:
The Patriot Press
Hyannis, Massachusetts

ISBN 0-939059-07-X

Color photography by Michelle Bosch
All other photography by Brian Cullity, unless otherwise noted.

Title page: Figure 1. Cleon and Elmer Crowell in the doorway of their workshop, c. 1927-1930. Elmer is holding a "white heron" and Cleon has an oversized Mallard. The pattern for the heron is dated 1927 and is illustrated in catalogue number 103.

Acknowledgments

An extraordinary amount of assistance was given by many people in putting this information and exhibit together. Everyone, from the Harwich Town Hall to the National Census Bureau, freely contributed information and provided assistance. Those who knew Elmer and Cleon eagerly consented to interviews are especially thanked for their patience and knowledge. Numerous auction galleries, dealers and collectors shared their records, provided catalogues and valued objects. Long distant calls to strangers were rewarded with an outpouring of help.

A few very special people warrant individual mention for their efforts above and beyond the call of duty:

to my wife, Nancy, whose encouragement and faith in me has provided the inspiration to complete this project in record time,

to my mother, Rosanna Cullity, for aiding in more ways than can be listed in this short space - for providing information, finding invaluable objects, photographs and sources and even making long distant trips in a pinch,

to Gigi Hopkins for the enthusiasm, advice and "eyes" of an artist, and for the technical assistance rendered with the contribution of her superb article and numerous conversations about the carvings,

and to those individuals who wish to remain anonymous but were most instrumental to the success of this endeavor.

The following people also contributed greatly to the show but space, unfortunately, does not allow me to elaborate upon the services that were provided. My deepest appreciation to:

Karen Aude, Bill Bourne, Richard A. Bourne, Tom Bourne, Lucy Butler, Ron Burroughs, Ralph Cashen, Lisa Compton, Walter D. Cullity, Craig Edwards, Philip DeNormandie, Robert C. Eldred, Ruth Erickson, Eric Farham, Mary Gould, Gary Guyette, Marion Halperin, Ted Harmon, Linda Higgins, Donald B. Howes, Susan Klein, Ned Meany, Richard Miller, Al and Judy Minucci, Pauline Mitchell, Rob Moir, Elliot Orr, Jackson Parker, Jim Parker, Charlotte Price, Mrs. Eleanor Prouty, Ann Treat Reynolds, Donald Scothorne, Bob Shaw, Nancy K. Shaw, Debra Strain, Beverly Thatcher, Vickie Uminowicz (and Titcomb's Book Shop), Jane Cashen Walker, Ted and Alotta Whitney.

The Sandwich Animal Hospital was wonderfully understanding and helpful in providing the services of their x-ray machine and technician for our wooden birds.

Heritage Plantation staff, as always, assisted in many crucial aspects of the show. Michelle Bosch deserves special thanks for the hours upon hours of labor in the darkroom and Alotta Whitney, Registrar, for her evenings and weekends of editing. Our Director, Gene A. Schott, has provided much support and many creative methods of funding this project. Others, who are more than deserving of praise, include: Bill Brock, Phil Dolan, Jim Cervantes, Dave Hartwell, Joe Piazzi, and Al Andrade and his crew.

The President of the Board of Trustees, Mr. Josiah K. Lilly, III, was most gracious and generous in providing a special grant for the publication of this catalogue. Other Board members are also thanked for their continuing support of our special projects: Mrs. Josiah K. Lilly III, William Banks, Charles E. Hartshorn, Jr., Frederick H. Hilton and Frank L. Nickerson.

Brian Cullity,
Curator, Art Museum

FOREWORD

The story of Elmer and Cleon Crowell is about hunting and decoys, the invention of decorative bird carving, market gunning, conservation, Cape Cod, cranberries and ART. Elmer Crowell has long been hailed as a master decoy maker; however, that is only a small part of the story. The lives of Elmer and his son, Cleon, spanned just about one hundred years and their creative period, over sixty years. Thousands of carvings were made by the two men, ranging from decoys to miniatures to weathervanes to leaping fish. A number of accounts have been published over the years, primarily examining the work of Elmer as a decoy maker. The goal of this exhibit is to chronologically explore the complete body of work of both men and to examine the stylistic and technical similarities and differences in their creations.

The recent acquisition, by Heritage Plantation, of over seven hundred patterns used by Elmer and Cleon to create their carvings precipitated this show. Ensuing research with the patterns, carvings, friends, acquaintances and documentary sources has revealed a reasonably coherent story of their lives, work, collaboration and sequential time frames for some of the carvings. An attempt was made to present not only the best of their work but also to seek out pieces that could be attributed to a given man for comparative purposes.

Additional information about carving techniques, marketing, brands and signatures, anecdotal material and other factors affecting their lives and work has also been included to present as complete a story as possible. A number of the conclusions drawn from a logical examination of the records has revealed some interesting and controversial aspects about the Crowell workshop: the ornamental carvings did not evolve from decoy carving, Cleon played a major role in the business and Cleon's participation may date from the very beginning of the business. This show will help clarify facts in an orderly manner and also give Cleon his due reward as a talented and prolific carver of decoys, miniatures and models. It will also present the Crowell workshop as capable of creating an extremely wide range of carvings; extraordinary for the time, and perhaps unchallenged to this day.

The legacy of these two men continues to this day. The Crowell "look" has probably been the most imitated in the twentieth century and the record smashing prices for the carvings are legendary. It can truly be said that decorative bird carving was invented in the humble workshop in East Harwich and has been the predominant influence on that art throughout the twentieth century.

INTRODUCTION

Beetleheads, gogglenoses, dipper-dappers, teeter-peeps and skunkheads: wild fowl come in all shapes and sizes and have as many names to match. It may seem preposterous to our minds, let alone tastes, but a brace of roasted snipe or plover was "one of the most luscious morsels to delight the epicurean palate" in the nineteenth century. "These (quail, woodcock, snipe, plover, etc.) are good roasted before a bed of coals, searing them first as in broiling meat. Impale each bird on a green stick, with a slice of bacon on the point of the stick over the bird. Thrust the butt of the stick into the ground, and incline stick toward the fire. Turn frequently."[1] Shorebirds and ducks were hunted relentlessly through the nineteenth century and into the first two decades of the twentieth before legislation restricted and finally outlawed the sale of migratory birds. However, that legislation did not come in time for the Labrador duck, passenger pigeon or the Eskimo curlew. All were extinct by 1914. In fact the last known Eskimo Curlew in New England was shot on September 5, 1913 at East Orleans, Cape Cod. This tragic story has another side however: one that concerns art - the art of the decoy.

GENERAL HISTORY OF MARKET GUNNING

The context in which decoys were first conceived, produced and used is important to the overall understanding of Crowell carvings. The art of decoy making stemmed from the hunting of wildfowl, just as the art form of scrimshaw making was derived from whaling.

The American wilderness of the eighteenth and nineteenth century offered a vast and seemingly unending supply of wildfowl for the hunter. Massive flocks of birds made yearly migrations to the northern nesting grounds, resting and feeding in the ponds and waterways of the New England coast along the way. The south shore, especially where the Cape and the Islands were thrust out into the ocean, were prime locations for these overflights and consequently became widely known as favored hunting spots. Initially, hunting was primarily for placing food on the family table. However, by the early nineteenth century a profound change in supply and demand was to occur. Two basic reasons drove these changes. The first was the skyrocketing demand for wildfowl to supply the restaurants of the urban cities burgeoning throughout the eastern coast. These birds, especially species such as the Eskimo Curlew, were considered great table delicacies. The second was fashion - a seemingly insatiable desire for bird feathers to decorate "me ladies fair head dress."

Market gunning, the profession of mass killing waterfowl for profit, was the inevitable American response. Although it is abhorrent to the twentieth century mind, the wholesale slaughter of waterfowl and shorebirds was a legitimate(and legal) source of income for hunters during the nineteenth century. Tales of the vast numbers of birds killed in these hunts abound and have been published by many authors. The Eskimo Curlew, mentioned earlier, passed over their migratory routes in enormous flocks that darkened the sky in the 1870's and 80's, yet was all but extinct forty years later. It is not the purpose of this exhibit to explore the history of gunning, other than the relationship to Cape Cod and Elmer and Cleon Crowell. Yet, gunning is important for one to understand the relationship to the creation of the sculptural masterpieces made by these hunters.

The market gunners used numerous techniques to lure and kill their game, almost all of which are illegal today. Large bore guns, baiting ponds and waterways, live decoys and spring shooting were but a few of the methods employed. All were legal. Carved decoys, or "blocks" were also employed, and have an ancient history of usage in North America. The word decoy is thought to be a contraction from the Dutch term "Endekooy" meaning a duck cage or trap used in the days before firearms were common. It is comparatively recent in origin.[2] Native Americans were the first to fashion models of birds to be employed as decoys. Beautifully preserved canvasback decoys fashioned from painted reeds and rushes and embellished with feathers were discovered in an archaeological dig in 1924. These decoys were fashioned by the Tule Eater's tribe in Nevada about one thousand years ago. Other carved Indian decoys from various tribes along the eastern seaboard are also known. The American hunter most likely learned decoy use and making from the Native American and readily adapted it to his own hunting methods.

Most hunters made their own decoys. They ranged from the crudest rough blocks of wood to finely carved and realistically painted sculptures. Two general types were made: floaters and stick-ups. Floaters refer to solid or hollow body carved ducks and geese that were made to be used on the water surface. Stick-ups are carved shorebirds (and occasionally geese) with a single wooden support which was stuck into the ground. Most decoys were used in groups, whether floating or as stick-ups. Sometimes they were referred to as "stools" which was the European name for the practice of fastening a live pigeon to a movable pole or perch (stool) as a lure to other pigeons.[3]

Decoy making in America increased in proportion to the demands made on the market gunners and peaked in the late nineteenth century. It was between 1850 and 1900 that the shorebirds and ducks were shipped by the thousands in barrels to the restaurants of the east coast. Wildfowl shooting was also a very popular sport as well as a business in this time and contributed to the demand for good decoys. Elmer Crowell lived, hunted, guided and carved in this period.

Pressure from concerned groups in the late nineteenth century started movements to outlaw this wholesale slaughter to try and prevent the extinction of birds. It was a difficult and bitter battle and lasted several decades pitting the hunters against concerned citizens. Several influential books were published on the topic, including

$2.50 a pair and canvasback ducks brought up to $3.00 a pair.[5] These were excellent wages at a time when a house on the Cape was valued at less than fifteen hundred dollars and a single season's work could easily bag several hundred fowl. Of the few gunning journals known from that period, all indicate that it was not at all unusual to bag several

FIGURE 2. Canada Geese about to be shipped to the market. Possibly Cape Cod, c. 1880-1910. Collection of Donald Scothorne.

"Our Vanishing Wildlife" by William T. Hornaday, in 1913. (A copy of this book was in Elmer Crowell's library and was a gift from Dr. John Phillips.) This movement eventually coalesced and is today The National Audubon Society.

Massachusetts outlawed the sale of game in 1912 after a tremendous struggle, especially by the market gunners of Cape Cod.[4] This had been a lucrative market. Prices for game were very attractive to the professional hunter of 1900. Typical wholesale prices to the New York market in 1910 (Hornaday p.310) showed that Golden Plover brought $2.50 to $3.50 a dozen, redhead ducks $1.50 to

dozen birds a day. Crowell states that he killed ninety-seven black ducks when he was fourteen years old. The next season he killed one hundred and eight black ducks.[6]

It was quite obvious to a few far sighted individuals that this sort of culling could not be sustained indefinitely. Tremendous pressure was brought on state legislatures to outlaw unfair game hunting. The result was the passage, in 1918, of the Federal Migratory Bird Act which effectively ended the wholesale hunting of game birds by outlawing their sale. Shorebird hunting was banned completely except for yellowlegs, black-bellied and golden plover - and those were included by 1928.

THE GUNNING HISTORY OF CAPE COD

Cape Cod was one of the more important regions in the northeast for market gunning. There were at least forty-four ponds on the Cape with professional gunning stands located on them from 1865 until 1929. Many of the locations had more than one stand. The toll of wildfowl taken on these locations was staggering. Elmer Crowell reported that he thought more than 1,000 ducks had been shot on the Upper Mill Pond in Brewster in 1927 alone.[7] More often, the bag for the season was between one to three hundred fowl per stand. This was Crowell's early environment; one to which he would develop an early and life-long affinity.

Many of these gunning stands were built and operated by wealthy individuals from Boston and the surrounding regions. For instance, Charles Ashley Hardy of Chatham and Wayland owned several gunning stands at various times. These men hired gunners to run the camps, care for the live decoys and do much of the shooting. Smaller operations were run by local hunters such as Elmer. (Not all the hunters were men. Phillips tells of a stand on Cliff Pond in Brewster which was owned by Mrs. Roland Nickerson and managed by Captain Nelson Perry. Mrs. Nickerson was an active gunner at the stand for many years).[8] Most of the stands kept flocks of live geese and ducks, which were used as decoys. Additionally, many of the ponds were baited with corn which would attract fowl to areas they normally avoided. Phillips reported that before baiting was used on Buck's Pond in Harwich, the yearly bag would average only seventy-five ducks. The average bag rose to 300 after the owner started baiting the pond with a bag of corn a day. Phillips also states that one site on Martha's Vineyard used two to three TONS of bait in a season.[9] Baiting caused the fowl to establish flight patterns to a particular spot chosen by the hunters. Among the species sought on the Cape were Mallard, Pintail, butterballs (Buffleheads), Ruddy, Scaup,

Teal, Widgeon, Redhead and all shorebirds. The Black Duck was the most plentiful and the principal game of these stands. They were so numerous that multiple kills could be made with one shot. Charles J. Eldredge remembered "one shot at Black Ducks that accounted for twenty-two with one shot."[10]

The practice of using live decoys on Cape Cod is discussed in some detail in two nineteenth century publications. "Scientific Duck Shooting in Eastern Waters" is an account of hunting practices on Wequaquet Lake in the town of Barnstable. The author, Russell Scudder Nye, asserts "all shooting here is done over live decoys"[11] and goes on to give a detailed account of the hunting techniques used for the Black Duck. He does, however, make a slight mention of wood decoys, but they are obviously of secondary importance. Hamblen Sears discusses how live decoys are trained and used on Cape Cod in "Fur & Feather Tails." Interestingly, the discussion

FIGURE 3. Brant hunting on the head of Pleasant Bay, Cape Cod, c. 1890-1920. This is a rare view of a "sink box." Collection of Donald Scothorne

large number of wooden ducks."[13] Elmer Crowell, the gunner, made decoys for himself and, after 1900, for other hunters. His son, Cleon, would later join him as a carver of both decoys and ornamental birds.

Figure 4. Shorebird hunting on Cape Cod, c. 1890-1910. Collection of Donald Scothorne.

ends with a brief rejoinder concerning the ethics of using live decoys versus wooden decoys. Indeed, even Phillips touches on the morality of hunting in this manner but eventually dismisses the question by rationalizing "With Black Ducks the so-called "slaughter" is not nearly as easy as it looks, for one false move will spoil the chances for a great shoot...The jump shoot is always difficult and usually complicated by the flying of one's own loose decoys." He continues:

"We are fortunate in Massachusetts in the manner of flight shooting for the better kinds of fowl. Martha's Vineyard is about the only place where real flight shooting was possible. Therefore, the development of stand shooting is a kind of natural outgrowth of rather unusual conditions. We are not especially proud of these methods of ours, they resemble too much the "hut" shooting of the French; but at least they are peculiar to New England and therefore of some interest to the history of American wild-fowl shooting."[12]

The point of this rather gruesome anthology is the other side of the story. Although the practice of using live decoys was considered a science and favored by most hunters on the Cape, they also used a goodly number of wooden decoys. The Cape has a long, proud, artistic history of shorebird and duck decoy making throughout the nineteenth century. Gunners would often carve decoys in the evening and other times of the year just as whalemen made scrimshaw in their spare time. For instance, Phillips reports that one stand on Walker's Pond in Brewster used 57 live geese and 48 live ducks, "besides a

Figure 5. Interior of a gunning club on Cape Cod, c. 1890-1920. Collection of Donald Scothorne.

Figure 6. The camouflaged goose blind and gunners of the same camp. Note the live goose decoys in the pen. Collection of Donald Scothorne.

ANTHONY ELMER CROWELL
1862-1952

Anthony Elmer Crowell was born December 5, 1862 in the village of East Harwich, Massachusetts. He had one brother, Everitt L. who was born in 1872 and died in 1895. His father, Anthony S. Crowell, was a mariner and cranberry grower who, by some accounts, did not particularly care for hunting. However, it is a matter of record that he gave Elmer his first gun at the age of 12 in 1874[14]. The land around East Harwich was rich in game and waterfowl in the late nineteenth century, and the numerous ponds and bays were a haven for sportsmen and market gunners from far and wide. Elmer thrived in this environment and, for the next thirty five years, devoted his pursuits to gunning in one form or another.

His father owned property on Pleasant Lake near the Crowell homestead and Elmer built a gunning stand there in 1876. He kept the stand for many years and shot ducks, geese and occasionally, shorebirds. He also hunted on the shores of Pleasant Bay which was only one mile from his house in the other direction. Some accounts have him making decoys at the early age of twelve or so, but Crowell himself states his preference was for live decoys. He kept flocks of both geese and ducks and later cared for the same for Charles A. Hardy and John Phillips.

Much has been written about Elmer's duck and goose hunting, but he was also enthusiastic about hunting upland game and fishing. He is remembered telling stories

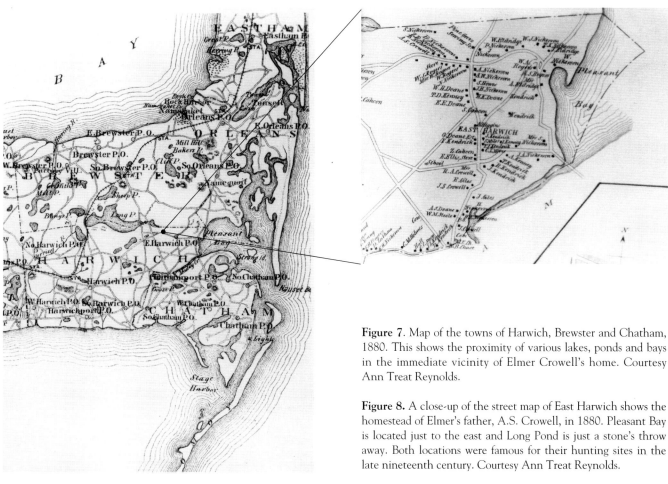

Figure 7. Map of the towns of Harwich, Brewster and Chatham, 1880. This shows the proximity of various lakes, ponds and bays in the immediate vicinity of Elmer Crowell's home. Courtesy Ann Treat Reynolds.

Figure 8. A close-up of the street map of East Harwich shows the homestead of Elmer's father, A.S. Crowell, in 1880. Pleasant Bay is located just to the east and Long Pond is just a stone's throw away. Both locations were famous for their hunting sites in the late nineteenth century. Courtesy Ann Treat Reynolds.

FIGURE 9. John C. Phillips hunting shorebirds, c.1900-1925. This may have been taken on the Cape. Note the tin decoys to the side of the dug-out hole and the "stick-ups" near the water's edge. Courtesy of Gary Guyette, Guyette & Schmidt, Inc.

about building quail runs and shipping the plucked game in iced barrels to New York City.[15] Other tales about quail and grouse hunting are related by Crowell in his 1947 article "Cape Cod Memories."

Elmer was "gunning for the market" by the year 1884[16]. Shorebirds, primarily Yellowlegs, were the game at that time. By the next year he was hunting Black Ducks with his new hammerless shotgun and using both live and block decoys. He recalls, in an article written in 1947, the numbers of Black Ducks taken every season and vividly describes the use of live decoys. Carved decoys, or blocks, are mentioned only once in this recollection. This is of particular note as this appears to indicate that Crowell's decoy making did not commence with earnest until fairly late in his career. He, like other hunters, preferred live decoys with a smattering of carved ones thrown in.

Crowell began working for Mr. Charles Ashley Hardy at the Three Bears Club on Pico Point on Pleasant Lake in East Harwich, around 1889. The "Three Bears" were Charles Ashley Hardy, G. Herbert Windeler (architect) and Loring Underwood. Elmer's relationship with Hardy would last for many years and play an instrumental part in his future profession as a carver. He was responsible for taking care of the large (50) flock of geese decoys at the Three Bears Club as well as gunning for the club. Crowell relates an ingenious method of using the tame geese in his 1947 "Cape Cod Memories" article: "We built pens on the hill in back of the blind, attached electric wires to them, and ran the wires down to the blind. We had four boxes on the inside of the blind with electric buttons.

When we saw a bunch of geese coming we pushed the buttons and the trapdoor would fall down and out would come the flyers (tame geese). They would fly out over the lake, and sometimes they would join the bunch of wild ones and bring them to the beach. It was a success and we had good shooting for a number of years."[17]

They also baited in front of the blinds at the lake. "It stopped the Black Ducks from going south, so the ponds were full of ducks; the shooting was great. But we could not sell them in the markets, as the law cut it out. Soon the law cut out the live decoys, and that was the end of good shooting here."

Crowell continued to hunt for the market and care for the Three Bears Club for the next several years. He ran his own stand, just a half mile from the Three Bears Club, from 1879 until 1909. He also had control of a gunning stand just north of his called the Greenland Point Blind. His own remarks in later life clearly indicate that this period was the highlight of his various careers. He loved hunting. It was a passion for Crowell, one that would continue until the passage of gaming laws restricted his activities. However, Crowell was to enjoy the employment of another very influential person before those laws were passed. Dr. John Charles Phillips of Beverly and Boston was an avid gunner. Phillips' position as a wealthy doctor, hunter and chronicler of sport and market hunting would provide Crowell with the vehicle to transform his carving pastime into a thriving business.

Phillips hunted on Chatham, Cape Cod, in the years 1898 and 1899 when he probably first met Elmer. Phillips also bought and developed a hunting camp on Wenham Lake in Beverly in 1898. He brought Crowell to that camp as caretaker and gunner in 1900. The "Wenham Camp Score Book" for that year begins: "Early notes (up to September 25), kept by E. Crowell, who gunned here for the first time."[18] This date has been erroneously published in the past as 1898. Crowell was to work seasonally for Phillips as a gunner for the next ten years. He was at

FIGURE 10. John C. Phillips in his hunting stand. This photograph was on the wall of the Crowell workshop for many decades. Collection of Philip DeNormandie.

Wenham from 1900-1905 and at another Phillips' camp on Oldham Lake in Pembroke in later years.

Phillips speaks of Crowell and his work at Wenham in "A Sportsman's Scrapbook":

"Elmer Crowell of Cape Cod fame officiated at this camp for many years and introduced us into all the niceties of live decoy lore. He showed us how to build a proper duck coop, how to rig a 'runner' far out into the pond that always worked, and how to train a duck to catch corn in its bill as cleverly as a dog catches a biscuit. And he could shoot, too, could Elmer. I can see him now dodging about the stand and pitching ducks into the air with amazing dexterity, never for a moment taking his bulging eyes off the circling flock of wild ones. Then when the shy birds finally 'took the water,' the first thing Elmer did was to tear off his coat in a sort of crouching position, but eyes to the front always. The rest of us would often get flurried and want to shoot too soon, but not Elmer. He had a calming influence and would never 'give the word' until just the right moment. And Elmer used to decorate Wenham Camp with all sorts of mythical-looking birds, whittled out and suspended from the ceiling so that they revolved solemnly around if you blew a puff of smoke their way, and we kept a sketch-book where he contributed drawings depicting important events. It was here, too, that Elmer made those most surprising technical suggestions on paper at the time when Drs. C. and W. were reading manuscript of their book on genito-urinary surgery. These I fear are forever lost to the followers of AEsculapius."[19]

It was here that Crowell developed a close relationship with Alfred B. Gardner of Accord. Gardner, who was born in 1881, was also employed by Phillips as a gunner and manager of the camp at Oldham from 1905 until 1909. Gardner later took it over under lease for Stone & Webster and ran it for a few more years. He and Crowell shot geese together and became good friends. They continued to visit each other for many years after Crowell had stopped gunning.

Gardner was also a neighbor and close friend of Joe Lincoln, the decoy maker of Accord. Much has been speculated about the influence Lincoln may have had on Crowell's work, especially the miniatures. However, Crowell was carving superb miniatures by 1894 and it may

FIGURE 11. Gunning skiff at Wenham or Oldham Lake. The figure in the boat is probably Elmer or Dr. Phillips. This photograph was another that Elmer had displayed in the workshop. Collection of Philip DeNormandie.

FIGURE 12. Alfred (Fred) Gardner fishing, c. 1900-1905.

be that the influence was the other way around. Either way, it seems clear that the two were acquainted. Phillips, for instance, had both Lincoln and Crowell decoys in his gunning stands and the proximity of the Oldham camp to Lincoln is difficult to ignore.

Crowell and Gardner remained lifelong friends, often reminiscing about "Them good old days" at Oldham. The painting illustrated in catalogue number 97 was a present to Gardner and relates an early incident at the Oldham

FIGURE 13. Fred Gardner with live geese decoys at Oldham Camp, 1905.

Camp. Gardner later tried his own hand at carving decoys and also made a number of ornamentals which were obviously influenced by the Crowell "look."

Phillips maintained these camps for decades and brought associates along to hunt as often as his schedule would permit. His meticulous records of the camp at Wenham provide us with a wealth of details about Crowell and how the stand was run day to day. Elmer usually arrived at the camp, by train, between early to mid September and would immediately begin work on the shooting stand: "In the fall it was a real occasion when Elmer or Eli (Eli Rogers, another gunner from the Cape) arrived, the camp opened up, the duck blocks anchored off in front and the stand 'brushed' up. A week or more was usually consumed in getting things ship-shape, and these were happy times.."[20]

Phillips gives a very good description of a typical stand which is worth quoting:

"The typical Massachusetts goose stand consists of a camp large enough to sleep six or eight men, usually built on the pond shore directly back of the stand fence or 'breastworks.' The breastworks often extend along the pond shore for some distance on both sides, and it is customary to keep the duck beach more or less separate from the goose beach. This beach, which is artificial, may have one or two considerable points. It is sand-covered in most cases and used primarily to peg out the decoys so they will show better from off in the pond. The beach also serves to keep wild geese or ducks from getting in too close for a shot during the night. It is a kind of a common meeting ground and washing-up place for all the live decoys and much care is lavished upon it.

Some decoy geese are also kept in the stand, mostly the old mated pairs, while the goslings or flyers are in pens on higher grounds.....In the old days a team of 15 or 20 geese was large. Now 50 to 100 is the usual number..

Besides the live geese, a fleet of wooden or canvas-covered blocks or "goose-woods" is anchored out in the

FIGURE 14. The Crowell and Gardner families at Accord, c. 1925.They are left to right: Elmer's wife, Laura, Elmer, Fred Gardner, Gardner's mother "Grandma Leonard," Mrs. Gardner, Nellie Mae Crowell (Cleon's wife), Eleanor Gardner (Fred's daughter) and Cleon and his daughter, Dorothy, in front.

pond at some distance from the stand. ...

The foregoing will show there is considerable investment in goose-stands today, taking into account land on the shore, camps, coops, fences, live geese, live ducks, and canvas-covered or wood decoys."[21]

FIGURE 15 and 16. Two views of Dr. Phillip's hunting camp at Oldham Pond, 1905.

FIGURE 17. Live geese decoys at Oldham Camp, 1905.

One of the hazards of using live decoys was the chance that you would kill your own tame duck or goose. Phillips wrote this poem about just such a sad occasion that happened to Elmer in 1903:

CROWELL'S LAMENT

She was the best of all the flock
And now she's stiff and stark
No more you'll hear her "wirey" quack
off Wenham Camp, "just dark."

A straying pellet from my gun
Has laid the victim low,
It almost makes me weep to think
that I have dealt the blow.

Full many a wary Black duck
She's lured within my shot,
and now a cold and clammy grave
Has got to be her lot.

We'll give her decent burial
and hope that in the sky
She'll meet with other Duck Decoys
in the sweet Bye and Bye.

The camp was also used for hunting grouse, quail and pheasants. Crowell's job for Phillips was similar to that at the Three Bears Club on Cape Cod: to maintain the camp, serve as a gunner, guide and overseer. In addition, he kept records of all wild fowl that were seen, shot or wounded and he also made decoys in his spare time- decoys that were so good that Phillips and the other hunters begged him to make more. Crowell's own account of that fateful occurrence was told in a 1914 interview in the Boston Globe.[22]

"He raised ducks and trained them for live decoys to be used in his blind at the local lakes, and by watching their movements he shaped and painted his own wooden decoys true to nature. His theory was to attract a flock of birds to alight among them each decoy should be different from the other in position of its head and neck.

During several seasons about a dozen years ago, Mr. Crowell was in charge of Dr. John Phillips' gunning camp at Beverly, and upon visiting East Harwich afterwards Dr. Phillips expressed such admiration for some hastily made decoys that Mr. Crowell made a few better ones for the doctor's personal use.

He also whittled out a small miniature bird which attracted Dr. Phillips favorable notice to the extent that he had a dozen made for his den."

Elmer's artistic flair was apparent from an early age and not limited to carving. In 1876 he took twenty four painting lessons from Miss Emily King of Middleboro who spent summers in Harwichport. They cost his parents $1.00 each. The still life illustrated in catalogue number 94 was most probably done during that time. The painting of Wading Place Bridge (cat. number 95) was painted fourteen years later as a wedding gift to his wife and shows remarkable improvement. This painting remained one of his treasured possessions, hanging over the mantel, until he died in 1952. His style was very much in the "folk art" tradition although paintings done late in life are actually

FIGURE 18. Photograph of Elmer as it appeared in 1914 in the Boston Sunday Globe. This same photograph is published in Connett's book as having been taken in 1898, but that date is probably in error.

more naive in appearance than his earlier attempts. Most of Crowell's paintings relate to hunting scenes and the birds he sought. Many are depictions of actual events and are quite humorous.

Crowell also started carving at an early age. He tells of making and painting miniature birds when he was twenty years old in 1882.[23] He showed them to a "woman bird carver in Boston" who encouraged his work. These birds are described as being carefully painted and would indicate that Crowell had a long standing and well established hobby before he was to make carving an occupation at the age of fifty-one. A few accounts mention limited decoy making in these early years and it would seem natural that both would have occupied his time. There are no known signed decoys from this period.

Crowell's association with Dr. Phillips signaled an important change in his life. The carving he had done as a hobby since 1882 would now become his avocation with the assistance of Phillips and his associates. Elmer was now being asked to sell his decoys and miniatures to other hunters. This also probably signals the beginning of the "Crowell" look. Examination of dated miniatures reveals the rapid transition and sophistication the carvings underwent in a few short years. Early decoys and miniatures quickly evolve from rather heavy bodied fowl to the sleek, realistically sculpted and painted birds we associate with the Crowell workshop.

Crowell stopped working for Phillips around 1910, but they continued to have a close relationship over the years. Phillips bought decoys and ornamentals from the workshop until the thirties, when he died. One order, placed in 1930, was for two mantel birds (Willet and beetlehead) and a pair of "gun Heads" for a total of $65.00. Phillips writes affectionately about Crowell in several of his publications and also briefly mentions Cleon's role in the business: "A few days ago I had a letter from Elmer which shows that he carries about with him a lingering weakness for Wenham. He says, 'As I read it (the Wenham Camp Shooting Log) the old days come back when there was plenty of grub in the larder and the little wicker jug under the bed. Them were the days, alright! I wish I could live them over once more, but they have gone forever.' And he adds that he and his son are still 'stubbing' around in the old shop, turning out vast numbers of duck decoys as usual. And that reminds me that Elmer had a vocabulary all his own and needed no Websterian help to lend color to his conversation. He had an imaginary month called 'Auguary' which was supposed to include all the wildest and duckiest weather. So when Elmer would poke his head outside before blowing out the lamp and remark that it 'sure did look like Auguary,' we turned over and went to sleep with the promise of dirty weather ahead."[24]

The demand for his work was not restricted to decoys. He was carving shorebirds, miniatures and ornamentals from the very beginning. The earliest carving known to be made by Crowell is the miniature Canada goose in the collection of Shelburne Museum dated 1894. Other early non-decoy carvings include numerous miniatures from 1900-1905 and the mackerel in the collection of Heritage Plantation which is dated 1903.

Elmer's passion was hunting, but cranberry farming was his bread and butter during this period. The gunning stands of Phillips and Hardy were seasonal and other activities were needed to bring in a steady income. (The market value of the 362 birds shot at Phillips camp in 1901 was only $139.75 . p. 42-43) Although he calls himself a mariner at the time of his first marriage in 1890, he was officially referring to himself as a farmer in 1891 and cranberry farmer from 1900 through 1912. These facts are revealed in the Federal census of 1890, 1900 and 1910 and from the Vital Statistics of the town of Harwich. Crowell also is listed as a cranberry farmer in the 1901 Harwich Directory.

Elmer and his first wife, Laura, lived with Edward Doane, Laura's father. Doane was listed as the head of the household in 1900, but this was reversed by 1910. Crowell owned a horse and carriage from 1890 through 1912 in addition to a bicycle he purchased in 1902. No records can be found that indicate that Elmer owned cranberry bogs, so it is assumed that he worked for one of the many cranberry companies located in the mid Cape region. He did have

FIGURE 19. Signature on the reverse of the carved mackerel, catalogue number 89.

ten acres of woodland which was probably the property on Pleasant Lake used as a gunning stand.

Additionally, like many Cape Codders, he supplemented his income from a variety of other sources. He raised poultry, had an orchard and served as a guide for hunting and fishing parties on the Cape. Cranberry farming, however, was his primary source of income for the years 1891 through 1912, with some help from his carvings after 1900.

Crowell never sold any carvings prior to his association with Dr. John C. Phillips in 1900. The employment at Wenham gave Elmer the opportunity to sell, not only to Phillips, but to all the other wealthy associates who came to the camp to hunt. These men included Drs. Cunningham, Sanborn, Coffin, Watson, Townsend, Barns and Musgrave and and other well known names such as Saltonstall, Kendall, Boardman, Brooks, Bigelow and Oliver. Dr. Cunningham remained a friend and customer throughout Crowell's lifetime.

Crowell was using wooden decoys at Wenham and numerous entries in Phillips' Wenham Lake Shooting Record attest to that fact: "Season 1903 - October 8th: Drizzling rain. South to Southeast wind. About 5:30 a bunch of 24 Blacks came in from the North and lit to blocks" and "December 8th (1904) Ther. 16, wind West. Pond all frozen tight. Cut out the Golden-eye blocks today."[25] Crowell relates in 1926 that his talent (at making decoys) became apparent when he started working for Phillips. "While he was connected to a private camp one time, there was trouble with the decoys. They didn't seem to decoy. The ducks refused to take them seriously.

"I can make better decoys than those," said Mr. Crowell, and he did. His employers bought them, and told their friends, and now his birds are everywhere."[26] Crowell's fame as a talented decoy maker spread quickly throughout the hunting community and orders for decoys and miniatures were soon forthcoming. His decoys were regarded as so special that it was said some hunters kept them in special cases to protect them.

Elmer Crowell gave up cranberry farming and started carving for a living in 1912. This may have been accomplished with a little help from his friend Charles Ashley Hardy. The Hardy family oral history relates that Charles Hardy felt that Elmer's carvings were just too good to be used as decoys and so funded Crowell to set up business full time as a decoy and ornamental carver. The financing was probably used to purchase woodworking machinery, a work bench and carving tools. A treadle operated bandsaw with wooden wheels was still in use during the 1930's according to neighbors who remember the shop. The workshop itself was made from an old chicken coop attached to the barn and barely 10 by twenty feet in size. The remainder of the barn was used as a garage and for storage.

This was a major transition for Crowell. He was fifty years old and starting on a new career - not an easy task. The year 1912 appears to be a key date in the Crowell chronology. It signals a change in his own perception of his workmanship. Early carvings by Elmer are signed "Maker" - a reflection of craftsmanship and the pride of making an individual object. Crowell begins using the word "manufacturer" in 1912 to reflect his entry into the business world. Indeed, the town of Harwich begins to tax Elmer for "Value of Machinery used in a Manufacturing Establishment" and for "Persons Whole Stock in Trade" the very next year. The value of the machinery was $50.00 from 1913 until the last entry in 1939. The 1920 Federal census lists Crowell as "manufacturer of decoys" and it is used again when Crowell remarries in 1927 after the death of his first wife in 1925.

Logic would lead one to conclude that 1912 identifies the first use of the "MFR" ink stamp. It would also seem to indicate that the "Maker" mark preceded that "MFR" mark. The earliest known use of the oval brand, coincidentally, is also 1912. This is found on the Great Blue Heron Crowell made for Mrs. Charles Hardy and now in the collection of Shelburne Museum. Again, logic would lead one to conclude that the oval brand was made the year of his entry into business full time.

Crowell's brief experiment of marketing his work with the Boston sporting goods store of Iver Johnson coincides with the years 1912-1913. Again, it would stand to reason

FIGURE 20. Base of Great Blue Heron, 1912. Courtesy The Shelburne Museum, photo by Ken Burns.

that Crowell would attempt to try this line of expansion in the early years of his business. He states in 1914 that: "after receiving numerous orders for his models from sportsmen acquaintances Mr. Crowell decided to place some on sale with a sporting goods company."[27] These Black Duck decoys with the white "Iver Johnson" stencil are well known in the decoy world. They exhibit masterful painting qualities and are useful in determining Crowell's early style of work. (catalogue number 11) They also differ markedly from the form of the earlier chip carved Black Ducks and show a mature and confident hand.

A relative perspective of the amount of work produced by the workshop can be gained in examining the value of the "stock in trade" (his inventory of decoys, ornamental carvings and rough stock) over the years. This figure ranged from a low of $70.00 in 1913 to a high of $460.00 in 1923. This was during a time when the value of his homestead was calculated at $1,000.00. Quite a few ornamentals!!

The production of the shop during these years grew to a phenomenal degree. Back orders were the rule and the carvings eventually suffered from the speed and pressures of demands on the workshop. Several have described the business during the 1930's as "almost mass produced."[28] Incomplete records show that 153 decoys and 96 heads were made in 1928 and 280 decoys were made the following year. In addition, numerous sets of miniatures, mantel birds and other carvings were also being produced. All carvings were still accomplished in the same laborious manner; however, the size, shape and paint application changed to conform to the demands of the numerous orders.

Elmer mentions that the ornamentals were a significant aspect of the business by 1926 and decoy making was on the wane. "I don't get much time to make decoys nowadays, though, ..The ladies keep me too busy making the small birds for them; there is better money in them, too. I make them for schools a lot, and gardens, and houses, and for private collections."[29] The first sets consisted of 48 native Cape birds according to the same article. However, by 1933, the miniatures were being produced in the more familiar groups of seventy-five. These consisted of twenty-five ducks, twenty-five shorebirds and twenty-five songbirds.

Crowell's reputation brought him business from rich and poor alike. He is known to have assisted a number of local hunters and carvers by painting their decoys. Several examples of this work are illustrated in Mackey's book on page 81.[30] The Crowell paint is unmistakable on these poorer quality carvings and even machine turned decoys. Likewise, he also painted bodies for better known carvers. Cleon, his son, related in a 1950's conversation that they would receive unpainted decoys from Henry Keyes

Chadwick on Martha's Vineyard. These were shipped to them screwed to the interior of barrels. They would be painted in the Crowell workshop and shipped back to Chadwick.[31] A number of entries in the order books are for repainting decoys (at $1.00 each) and one request is to "Repaint 6 decoys into Goldeneyes."

The fame of the Crowell carvings spread throughout the country. The work from the shop was shown at the Boston Sportsman Show for a number of years. Cleon attended these week long events starting in 1925, the first year they were held. Customers at the East Harwich shop included Henry Ford (he visited the Cape in 1926 and stayed at the Blue Lantern Tavern in Barnstable)[32] the Rockefellers and the DuPonts. Associates from the Wenham Camp also continued to patronize the shop throughout the 1920's and 1930's. The artist and ornithologist, Roger Tory Peterson also visited in the later years. Joseph C. Lincoln, the author, was a close friend and used Elmer as the central character in a 1933 novel titled

"Queer Judson" which brought Crowell additional publicity.[33] He was often the subject of newspaper interviews and was a master of public relations. He had post cards made, during the thirties, using a photograph of him at his workbench. His son, Cleon, who was working full time in the shop, was seldom, if ever, mentioned in these interviews. It wasn't until the late thirties, when Elmer was slowing down, that Cleon's role becomes evident.

The fame and publicity accorded to Elmer never appeared to change the man from the warm, genial and patient individual that he was. He is remembered as being especially kind with children, often giving them carvings to play with. These have long since been lost, but the memories remain strong in the minds of those who knew him. He enlisted the help of older boys to assist him in retrieving the cedar logs from a local swamp which were needed for the carvings. They, in turn, would often present him with a duck or two they had shot in the local ponds.[34]

FIGURE 21. Elmer Crowell in the workshop, c. 1930. Note the miniatures mounted on dowels to facilitate the painting. The holes seen in the bellies of miniature birds were made from the metal pins on the ends of the dowels. Collection of Steve Tyng.

He mentions one such present in a letter to his old friend, Fred Gardner, in 1947: "I had 2 Black ducks given me and that is all the game I have had for a long time."

Sadly, Elmer's first wife, Laura, died in 1925. In 1927 he married his second wife, Elizabeth W. Wadsworth from Providence, Rhode Island. The neighborhood children remember, fondly, the many evenings they would watch through the window as Elmer would crank up his Victrola and he and Betty would waltz in the kitchen. He was a superb dancer and was always popular at the local gatherings.

Elmer continued carving until the late thirties when his rheumatism started to hamper his ability to hold a knife. A brief article published in 1939 states: "Now his son, Cleon S., also very clever with his hands, carves most of the birds from his dad's patterns and sketches."[35] By 1943 Elmer had stopped work altogether and Cleon carried on the business by himself. Elmer was then eighty one years old. He writes to his old friend Fred Gardner in 1947: "I have not done any work for four years my hands got so bad with rheumatics I had to quit." He was not idle, however, for he continued his hobby of painting on canvas and board until 1951. He was also known to have paint decorated furniture

Figure 22. Elmer Crowell in the workshop, c. 1933. This photograph was used by Crowell for advertising on a postcard. It was also published in the Cape Cod Times in 1933. Collection of Gigi Hopkins.

with floral scenes.

The publicity for the shop continued, even though Elmer was no longer able to make the carvings. He is pictured in Eaton's "Handicrafts of New England" in 1949 - poised as though he were painting a shorebird, but it is very obviously a contrived photograph. Another often published photograph, also taken in 1949, pictures him before a window with a number of carvings on the table and Elmer holding a brush. Elmer was then eighty-seven years old and had but two years to live. He had long ago stopped working, although he was still painting on canvas.

His rheumatism made life difficult and he and his beloved wife, Betty, needed a full time housekeeper by 1947. His wife died two years later, in 1949, and Elmer passed away on January 1, 1952. Sadly, for all the fame Elmer realized during his life, he never had the fortune. His estate consisted of two oil paintings, a potbellied stove and his carving tools. Value: two hundred dollars.

FIGURE 23 and 24. These two photographs of Elmer were included in a 1926 article about the shop in the Cape Cod Magazine. The outside view shows him holding a Blue Jay on a stick.

FIGURE 25. This photograph has been widely published. It was taken in 1927 and shows Elmer outside his shop with an array of carvings that would make most collectors weep. Note the preening Black Duck decoy sitting on the slat goose. Also, carved wingtips and tail feathers can be clearly seen on the Redhead in the foreground.

FIGURE 26. Elmer with a preening "Jack Curlew" ornamental, c. 1930. He wrote on the back: "This is one of my models made from wood and painted by me Elmer Crowell."

FIGURE 27. Elmer Crowell, 1949.

CLEON STANLEY CROWELL
1891–1961

FIGURE 28. Cleon Crowell holding a Black Duck decoy, c. 1945-1950. This photograph was taken in Elmer's old house where Cleon kept his sample miniatures. Some can be seen on the shelf behind him. This was also the room where much of the painting was done.

Cleon Stanley Crowell was born in 1891, the only child of Elmer and Laura Crowell. Unlike Elmer, nothing is known of the early childhood of Cleon. It would be safe to assume that Cleon participated in activities with his father, perhaps even visiting with him at one of the camps in Wenham or Oldham Pond. He knew Dr. Phillips and is mentioned in his book "The Shooting Stands of Eastern Massachusetts." Undoubtedly, as with typical Cape families, Cleon assisted his father in the various tasks associated with the cranberry farming, raising fowl and perhaps even assisted with some of the guiding. It would

Crowell and his son, Cleon, have concentrated on this work for more than 25 years and have included fish among their carvings."[37] Another, published in 1951 speaks of Cleon: "His father has taught him through the years, because when he first started making his sets, in 1912, his son hovered around, eager to help, and is now carrying on, using the parental patterns."[38] Although the author of the article made it sound as though Cleon was a small child at the time, he was an adult and most likely worked for his father.

The degree to which Cleon assisted in the business in

FIGURE 29. Cleon Crowell. This is an early photograph of Cleon returning from a duck hunt.

also seem to be a reasonable assumption that Cleon learned about carving and painting at an early age. Indeed, one article published in 1969 states that Cleon "started working at his father's side when he was only fourteen or so (1905)." No source is cited for that statement.[36]

It is safe to assume, however, that Cleon did start working, in some capacity, for his father in 1912. After all, he was twenty one years old, living at home and Elmer had just started a new business. A 1937 article states "Mr.

the earliest years is not known and has seldom been addressed. He lived at home until his marriage in 1917 and was at that time a chauffeur for a local family. He spent some time away from East Harwich while serving as a private in the armed forces during World War I. He returned to East Harwich in 1918 and continued his work as a chauffeur for two years. He resumed working for his father, full time, in 1920. An early photograph of the two (on the title page) shows Cleon holding a pintail decoy

A. E. CROWELL & SON

Makers of Carved Ducks and Game Birds

12 SOUTH STREET
HARWICH PORT, MASS.

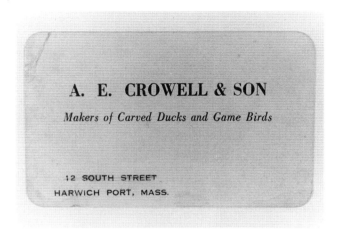

FIGURE 30. Cleon Crowell's business card, c. 1946-1961. Penciled notations on the back note prices: "Song birds (3" or less) Jay etc. $10.00. Ducks, shorebirds (3" or more) $15.00. Decoy size Mallard Etc. $35.00." Heritage Plantation collection

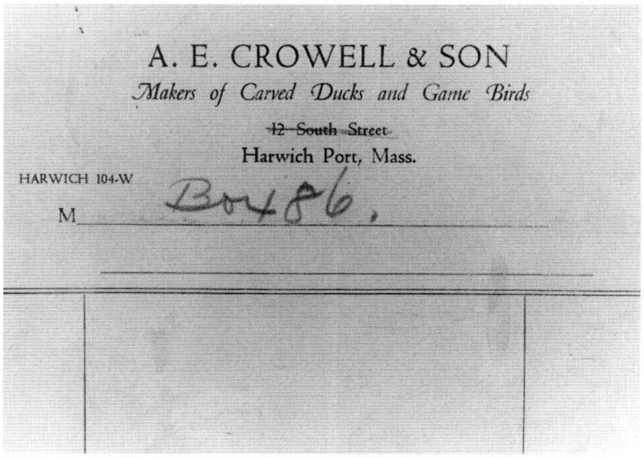

A. E. CROWELL & SON

Makers of Carved Ducks and Game Birds

~~12 South Street~~
Harwich Port, Mass.

HARWICH 104-W

M Box 86.

FIGURE 31. Billhead for Cleon Crowell, 1946-1961. Heritage Plantation collection.

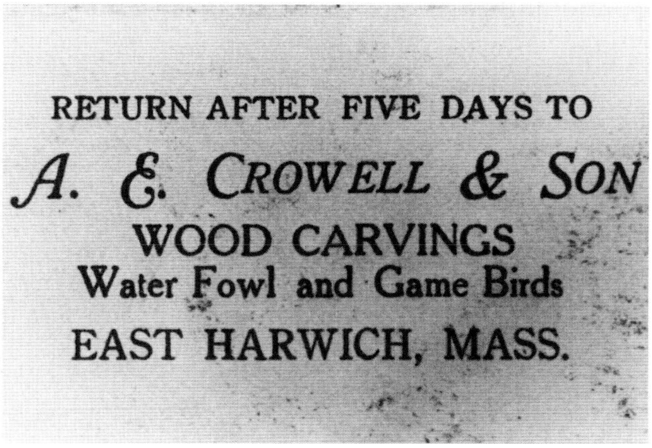

RETURN AFTER FIVE DAYS TO

A. E. CROWELL & SON

WOOD CARVINGS
Water Fowl and Game Birds
EAST HARWICH, MASS.

FIGURE 32. Envelope used by Cleon Crowell. Note that this has the East Harwich address, but was used in 1947 when he lived in Harwichport. Both addresses were used during this period.

and Elmer with a White Heron. The carving in Cleon's hand is an obvious indication of his role in the business as a working partner, making both ornamentals and decoys.

Elmer mentions a brief period after the war when the two of them operated a shooting stand on land Elmer bought on Bushey Beach Pond. They gunned the blind for a few years until the practice of using live decoys was declared illegal. Tax records for the town of Harwich indicate that Cleon had a flock of 20 geese from 1931-1933. It is possible that these were used as live decoys at the blind. Penciled notations are still visible on the walls of the workshop indicating when the first geese were either sighted or killed for the years 1925-1929.

Cleon and his wife, Nellie Mae, lived next door to Elmer in East Harwich until 1946. They moved to Harwichport in that year and kept a Harwichport address until Cleon's death in 1961. Some business cards and letterheads from that period are imprinted with "A.E. Crowell and Son/Harwichport". A few carvings are also signed in ink in the same manner. Cleon also continued to use the East Harwich address on business letterheads simultaneously and continued to work in the shop until his death. It is therefore possible to attribute all carvings with the Harwichport address as being from Cleon's hand and made after 1945. One possible exception to this exists. Cleon owned and was taxed for a "workshop" in Harwichport in 1939. His homestead, however, was Pleasant Lake. It is not known if Cleon used the workshop or rented the place. Both he and his wife were involved in the real estate business from 1946 until 1961.

Cleon's participation in the business, as mentioned earlier, was far greater than has previously been acknowledged. Numerous patterns bear his distinctive handwriting as do many of the earlier carvings. There is no question that he carried on in all aspects of the partnership- from making decoys and ornamentals to repair work and repainting. His late work, with a pronounced bulge to the bird's head, is often identifiable; however, it is virtually impossible to distinguish earlier carvings between the two men.

Cleon was well known throughout the region as an avid seeker and collector of local Indian artifacts and had a large collection at one time. He was a keen naturalist and shared time with children in the neighborhood as the first scoutmaster in the region. Roger Tory Peterson would stop when in the area and they would go birding together. Cleon's friend, Eric Farham, remembers well the time they were seeking Indian artifacts and Cleon dropped everything they were doing in order to watch the nearby seaducks. He also contributed to the large collection of bird skins used as models in the workshop.

The years from 1946 until his death were occupied with a variety of interests. He and his wife were involved in real estate and they were both quite interested in collecting antique glass. Cleon also continued carving throughout this period, even in the face of a paralyzing stroke suffered in the late fifties. He was able to overcome that handicap and resume carving and painting after many months of difficult self-rehabilitation. Cleon carved and painted until the very end. The order books reveal that he was taking requests to be filled well into the year 1962. He died on December 30, 1961.

FIGURE 33 and 34. Two views of Cleon Crowell painting miniatures, c. 1945-1960. These were taken in the room next to the kitchen in his father's house where Cleon often worked.

THE CARVINGS

First hand accounts of the Crowell shop invariably describe a pleasant atmosphere: the smell of cedar, wood chips and, above all, the warmth and humor of Elmer himself. It was a small space crammed with tools, a bench that ran the length of the building, a pot bellied stove and "the walls plastered with all kinds of things".[39] Most all the tools were hand powered, including the band saw, until the mid forties. A jackknife was the principal tool for the smaller carvings while a drawknife was used for the larger ones. The walls around the stove still bear the test marks of the oval brand and one spot is occupied with the "Iver Johnson" stencil. It was a simple, bare building with exposed beams and plank boards laid on the ground.

FIGURE 35 a & b. The Iver Johnson stencil and a test brand on the walls of the workshop. Courtesy Craig Edwards.

FIGURE 36. Interior of the workshop. This fabulous view graphically illustrates what words cannot convey about the shop. The walls are literally covered with tools, materials and patterns. Decoys in all stages of completion sit around (including a very Lincoln-looking goose) and chunks of cedar lie waiting to be fashioned into the famous birds. Heritage Plantation collection.

FIGURE 37 and 38. Two views of the exterior of the workshop, 1958. Heritage Plantation collection, gift of Mr. Elliot Orr.

Descriptions of their working methods are few. Early interviews simply mention the labor intensive whittling and painting required for the production of the birds. A few interviews mention that the paint was applied in several different coats, depending on the feather patterns of the bird. The traditional approach used by decoy makers was usually a one step process according to Joel Barber.[40] George Starr interviewed Elmer and reported:

"To gain the natural soft effect of a bird's feathering, a "tacky" technique was used. He (Elmer) explained to me that the final colors were laid on fairly thick over a thoroughly dried base coat. The bird was put aside until the paint became tacky, at which time the colors and shades were pulled together with a dry brush. The feathery effect produced by this method varies greatly from the kind of blending obtained when the paints are free flowing."[41]

The actual method of painting is described by Cleon in one of the original order books from the workshop:

FIGURE 39. Cleon painting a Kingfisher in the old homestead, c. 1955. This is a different view taken at the same time as figure 34. Collection of Donald B. Howes.

"1933
Painting a Summer Yellowleg

After priming coat put
in dots on head & neck and
blend in, paint wings
dark color and put in bars
under breast, also paint wing quills black. that's all
for this time. next time put
in feather markings and
put in the dark color and
blend these in, then paint
same color dots in. now
put in wing feather lines. When you put this bird on
the legs you put in the
white specks on the body
feathers. The dark color is
black, raw umber & burnt umber mixed together."

Much has been said about the use of plain house paints to achieve the realistic plumage on Crowell birds. Elmer may have used house paints in the beginning; however, he was using commercial oil paints by the 1920's and probably earlier. A photograph taken around 1925 shows him with numerous tubes of paint and two trays of miniatures which he is working on. Another photograph of Cleon painting a kingfisher shows commercial paints in the foreground. Differences can be seen when comparing earlier works with those from the later years in the quality of the sheen and brightness of colors. Regardless of the type of paint used, the fact remains that the Crowells were unsurpassed in the effect they achieved. The earlier paints do have a mellowness to them lacking in the later works.

FIGURE 40. Cleon at the bandsaw, 1957. Here he is cutting out the rough blocks to be shaped with a knife later on. Note the patterns hanging on the wall.

The earliest painting was done in a tentative, almost abstract, manner with laborious brush work. Feathers are not distinctly outlined; rather, they are formed as blended patterns. A distinctive change in the paint patterns and application is noticeable with later carvings. Feathers are delineated and specifically painted on the bird. It is believed that this change occurred after 1912 when the Crowells started using actual bird skins as their guide. Ornithology books were also used, especially the plates from Forbush rendered by Louis Agassiz Fuertes. Faster methods were employed such as "pouncing" the brush directly on the surface to achieve the desired patterns. The differences can be seen by comparing the redhead decoys in catalogue numbers 13-15.

Often, the painting was done in Elmer's house to avoid the effect of the dust in the shop, and to provide the room necessary for the two men to work. It also provided the warmth that was needed during the winter months. The workshop was quite small and was very crowded with both men in the cramped space. Some painting was also done in the shop as is evidenced by the photographs of Crowell. The workbench also has a build-up of oil paint where the brushes were cleaned on the legs. No information has been found to indicate that the Crowells used anyone else to either paint the carvings or do any other work for them. All evidence seems to substantiate that the work was done solely by the two men in the workshop.

Pine was the wood of choice for most decoy and decoy size carvings, although some are known to have been made with cedar. (catalogue numbers 11 & 17) The large chunks of wood were roughed out with an ax and hatchet and worked down on a shave horse. The finish work was accomplished with regular pocket knives.

Cedar was used almost exclusively for the bodies of the miniature carvings and was procured locally. These were left to cure in the barn and were later split with an ax into suitable sizes. The patterns were used to outline the form to be carved on the chunks of wood. These were then cut out with the bandsaw.

The patterns were drawn by both Elmer and Cleon on every conceivable material available. Many of the earliest examples are on the backs of cardboard political posters, hand lettered theater broadsides and calendars. A number of them of them are dated, and some have the customer's name in script. Various notations indicate sizes, use (decoy or ornamental), locations for usage (For the South Shooting, etc.) and occasionally the paints to be used for a particular carving. Some are drawn freehand and others have been traced from printed sources. The well known miniature feeding canvasback is taken directly from a copy of 1884 Chamberlain Cartridge Company Catalogue as are other birds illustrated in that publication. The tracing is so heavy on some of the illustrations that the image has been cut from the page. Both men used other printed material as sources for their patterns, especially the miniatures. A large sheaf of bird illustrations from varied sources was acquired along with the patterns. These included sportsmen magazines, National Geographic and Audubon publications and especially the colored plates by Louis Agassiz Fuertes. Dozens of these plates have penciled tracings around the birds.

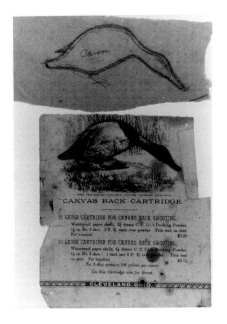

FIGURE 41 and 42 a & b. Chamberlain Cartridge Company Catalogue, 1884. Here, one can see where the feeding canvasback was traced to make the pattern for the miniature carved version. The other page has Elmer's signature and "My Game" in script next to the snipe.

FIGURE 43. X-ray of swimming Black Duck decoy (catalogue number 9). A carved dowel is used to attach the head on this early example. The two crossed nails are typical of Crowell construction, while the other nail indicates a repair.

X-ray examination of two dozen carvings revealed only a few construction details which appear to be consistent. All heads were attached with two angled nails, with one exception - the early sleeping Black Duck has a five inch spike driven through the head into the body in a manner typical of other decoy makers. Ninety percent of the nails used were 1¼ inches in length, a few were 2¼ inches long. The Crowells used both finish nails and nails with heads and a few of the earlier ones used square nails. . All full size decoys and carvings used dowels, along with the nails, to attach the head.

The black glass eyes which are generally found on earlier carvings, were attached by means of a small metal pin, the later paperweight eyes are cemented in without pins. Shorebird bills were attached by means of a wooden pin carved from the solid head. (Only a few shorebirds were x-rayed and the generalizations are speculative) The Crowells did use umbrella stays for legs. The stays are usually deeply embedded into the body and have gesso applied for shaping the knees. Larger ornamental carvings, such as the Wood Duck (catalogue number 46) and

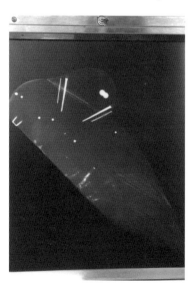

FIGURE 44. X-ray of sleeping Black Duck (catalogue number 9). This example shows clear evidence of being a working decoy. Square nails are used to attach the head.

Canada Goose (catalogue number 50), had wooden legs attached to the base. No differences in construction were noted between the works of Elmer and Cleon and no apparent changes were noted through the years other than the type of nails used.

Characteristics of the earliest decoys include fully carved primary feathers of the wings, carved tail feathers, rasped head and breast and special modeling to the head and neck. Preening, sleeping, contented, alert and swimming positions were frequently used to imitate natural postures of ducks, geese and shorebirds. The heads on ducks were often turned 15 to 20 degrees.

The early ornamental carvings were the recipients of the same labor of love - the only difference being the mounts they were placed upon. Shorebird decoys had only one central hole for sticking them into the sand, decoratives had realistic legs mounted on bases as did ducks and a few geese.

The carvings made for Crowell's special customers, especially Drs. Phillips and Cunningham and Charles Hardy, should probably be categorized separately. Many were made as full decoy size, but obviously, were never used as such. Most of the ducks have unpainted bottoms which is usually an indication they were not meant to be used as decoys. Others, such as the preening Black Duck, do have painted bottoms, yet are clearly intended as ornamental carvings, given their fragile nature. Most of these bear the oval brand (see fig 56) burned into the bottom and were probably made in the first years of Crowell's business, 1912-1915. No attempt is made in this catalogue to label full size duck carvings as either ornamental or decoys. They are simply described.

It is tempting to speculate that these wealthy friends assured Crowell's success by giving him considerable business orders. Dozens of carvings, owned by Phillips, Cunningham and Hardy, are known to collectors today. Crowell in turn, created the most spectacular group of painted carvings the hunting world had ever seen. His working decoys from this period (1900-1915) also show a degree of love, labor and art that is unparalleled in the decoy world. Wallace Furman, a Crowell friend and antique dealer, once expounded on the Crowell look. He is reported to have reflected on the fact that a Yellowlegs shorebird was so stupid that it would "come to a sock on a stick." Crowell had no reason, whatsoever, to create the sculptural masterpieces he did other than for the love of the art.[42]

Many authors have noted the decline in quality over the ensuing years. The demands for the Crowell's work exceeded their ability to produce the numbers of carvings requested from customers. Consequently, faster methods were developed to apply the paint and still retain the "Crowell look." The shape of the carvings also changed over the years and the miniatures began to grow larger and bulkier. The refined slender forms were too time consuming and gave way to quicker, but less appealing, carvings. Descriptions of the workshop in the late thirties invariably use the phrase "almost mass-production" to indicate the large numbers of carvings being made for customers around the country. Outstanding carvings were still being made for special people, but the overall quality lowered.

Six of the original order books from the workshop were recently acquired by Heritage Plantation and reveal a wealth of information concerning the carvings, customers, orders and working methods from the years 1927-1961. Some of the books are incomplete but a number of generalizations can be stated. A few of the orders are written by the customers with the prices or other notations added by Elmer or Cleon. All others are written by the two men.

Two facts are immediately clear when analyzing the order books. The first is the realization that all carvings were custom ordered, often with the customer's preference for a particular base, wing pattern, size or sex specified. The range of choices was staggering as can be seen with the tremendous variety of carvings shown in the exhibit.

The second fact is the important role of Cleon to the continuing success of the business. Most orders were recorded by both men until 1932-1933. Cleon appears to have handled all customers' requests after that date. The inference being that Cleon also did the majority of the actual work from the mid thirties on. This appears to be substantiated by several newspaper articles cited earlier. It is clear that Cleon was assuming more and more of the carving and painting work through the decade of 1930 and was doing all the work by 1944. A few of the earlier orders taken by Cleon can be matched with patterns, also in Cleon's hand. It can be assumed that if Cleon took the order and made the pattern, he most likely made the carvings. For instance, the oversized Canada Goose pattern illustrated in catalogue number 134 has "Storrow Model/1929" written in pencil in Cleon's handwriting. Cleon wrote the order for the gunning camp "Storrow's Camp/ 2 in shorter neck/3 doz large geese heads" during the year 1929.

Certain trends can be noted from the orders. Canada Geese weathervanes were popular from 1927-1933 and cost $35.00 each. Miniature mallard ducks on paperweights were fashionable from 1944-1946 and at least eighteen were made. Yellowlegs and "Beetleheads" were the most popular mantel birds from the late twenties through the thirties while Piping Plovers and other smaller shorebirds were requested with more frequency for the next two decades.

As a rule, decoy orders were recorded in one book and

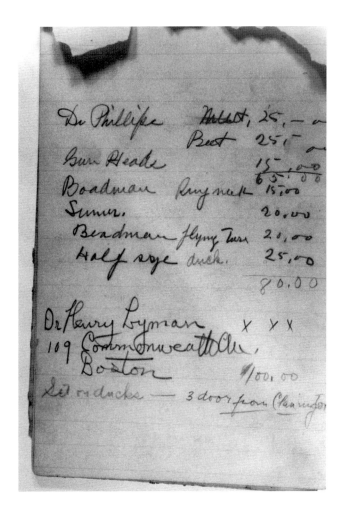

FIGURE 45. A page from the shop order book, c. 1930.

ornamental carvings were recorded in another during the earlier years. Later, when Cleon was working alone, all orders went together. Very few decoys were being made by the time Cleon took over the business. Green Wing Teals, Pintails and Mallards were the predominant requests.

Contrary to popular belief, the Crowells were able to sell their carvings for substantial prices, even in 1933. Their clientele tended to be professional individuals who did not suffer as much from the effects of the depression as did the rural residents of the Cape. Standard decoys brought $3.00 to $5.00 apiece while the life-size ornamental carvings sold between $35.00 and $50.00. The set of miniature ducks sold for $100.00 while the songbirds brought $75.00. It cost $1.00 apiece to repaint ducks and $.50 per head for replacements. While we may consider those prices to be a bargain today, they represented a substantial investment at a time when you could buy a brand new Ford for $750.00 (and a man would be happy to earn $15.00 a week).

The prices rose accordingly through the years. A pair of Mallards mounted on wood brought $15.00 a set in 1944 and were $35.00 in the late fifties. Miniatures went from $2.50 each in 1933 to $15.00 and decoys from $3.00 to

$10.00 to as much as $50.00 in 1960. The miniatures and ornamental carvings brought proportionately more than the decoys. They were far more labor intensive creations and the size made the painting difficult. Then too, their appeal was decorative and, therefore, a higher price could be charged than for working decoys.

Customers were often quite specific in ordering their carvings. A typical request might be "Yellowleg wing up $40.00" or "2 hump wood-duck on stump." Groups of decoys were most often ordered as "half and half" indicating half the number were to be male and the other half were to be female ducks. Cleon was often specifically asked to sign the carvings and on one occasion was requested to make "1 life size ruddy duck decoy" for $35.00 with "old stamp burned in." (This is probably the same decoy as catalogue number 20) Another very interesting note concerns carved features of decoys. One order from 1945 specifies Cleon to "cut out tail and wings" for $15.00. This is another reason for caution when trying to date carvings based on specific features.

Cleon kept a sample group of carvings in the house from which a customer could choose one to their liking. A number of these samples are clearly seen in the photograph of Cleon taken during the 1950's. (Figure 28) The shop books would often have entries reading "1 min. Partridge like mine" or "1 life size sandpiper on shell like mine, $35.00" (1959) Occasional orders mention "my base" which is believed to be the chip carved, stained bases seen on later type carvings.

Orders did, indeed, come from around the country and world. They continued to pour in until Cleon's death in 1961 when the final entries are made in the shop books.

FOOTNOTES:

1. Horace Kephart, "Camping" (New York, 1946), p. 319
2. Priscilla Lord, "Folk Art & Crafts of New England"(New York, 1965), p. 30
3. Priscilla Lord, p. 33
4. William Hornaday, "Our Vanishing Wildlife"(New York, 1913) p. 310
5. Ibid., p. 310
6. Eugene Connett, "Duck Shooting"(New York, 1947) p. 57
7. John Phillips, "Shooting Stands of Eastern Massachusetts" (Cambridge, 1929) p. 121
8. Ibid., p. 124
9. Ibid., p. 138
10. Ibid., p. 124
11. Russell Nye, "Scientific Duck Shooting in Eastern Waters" (Falmouth, 1895) p. 15
12. John Phillips, "Shooting Stands of Eastern Massachusetts"(Cambridge, 1929) p. 12
13. Ibid., p. 120
14. Connett, p. 56
15. Conversation with Mr. Ralph Cashem, 3/92
16. Connett, p. 57
17. Ibid., p. 33
18. John Phillips, "Wenham Lake Shooting Record"(Cambridge, 1929) p. 13
19. John Phillips, "A Sportsman's Scrapbook" (Boston, 1928) p. 33
20. Ibid., pp. 34-35
21. John Phillips, "Shooting Stands of Eastern Massachusetts" (Cambridge, 1929) pp. 7-9
22. see Boston Sunday Globe, 9/12/14 p. 61
23. see Cape Cod Standard Times, 4/9/33
24. John Phillips, "A Sportsman's Scrapbook"(Boston, 1928) p. 35
25. John Phillips, "Wenham Lake Shooting Records"(Cambridge, 1929) p. 89
26. see Cape Cod Magazine, 8/26, pp. 9-10
27. see Boston Sunday Globe, 9/12/14 p. 61
28. conversation with Mr. Ralph Cashem and Elliot Orr 3/92
29. see Cape Cod Magazine 8/26 pp. 9-10
30. William Mackey, "American Bird Decoys" (New York, 1965)
31. Conversation with Donald Howes 3/92.
32. see "Cape Cod Magazine" 8/26 pp. 9-10
33. see Cape Cod Standard Times, 4/9/33
34. Conversation Mary Gould, 4/92
35. Jack Frost, "A Cape Cod Sketch Book"(New York,1939)
36. see Yankee Magazine, 10/69 pp. 110-121
37. see Cape Cod Standard Times, 12/6/37
38. see Cape Cod Magazine, 1951 pp. 23-26
39. conversation with Elliot Orr, 3/92
40. Joel Barber, "Wild Fowl Decoys" (New York, 1934) pp. 68-69
41. George Ross Starr, Jr., "Decoys of the Atlantic Flyway" (New York, 1974) p. 160
42. conversation Richard A. Bourne, 4/92
43. see Cape Cod Magazine, 1951 pp. 23-26
44. see Guyette Auction catalogue 9/19/87, lots 715A-715H
45. conversation with Donald Howes, 3/92

THE CROWELL LOOK

By Gwladys Hopkins

The Crowell touch is unmistakable. It is seen both in the design of his work and in its execution, in the carving and in the paint. It is a far stronger signature than any brand, stamp or label.

There are four different steps or aspects to this type of carving. The first involves perception; the ability to see the natural world and have it come through the eyes. One must <u>see</u> the birds. Then there is design, the translation of the image into a pattern; how can one best freeze-frame the bird in motion and capture its beauty (or in the case of decoys, capture its brethren). Next comes the carry-though, the creation of the actual piece. This involves

The life-size hissing goose is a prime example of this. To the casual observer, it is simply a realistic piece. Anyone who had inadvertently stumbled upon a nesting gander recognizes the bird; in fact, even in wood, its threat is imposing. But here, too, is pure sculpture. Echoing contours move over and around the goose and its boulder; the piece is well balanced and has a pleasing symmetry. The carving, the knife work, is powerful; the shapes are strong and certain. The surface has a precise amount of detail; there is enough to engage the eye and keep it moving, but not so much that it detracts from the piece's overall form. The paint is masterfully handled; the colors

FIGURE 46. Canada Goose life size carving, 1917. Courtesy Alfred and Judith Minucci

freeing the bird from its block of wood - and finally - there is color. One must paint the wood in such a manner that it reads as soft feathering.

Each of these is a separate specialty, and the Crowell carvings, the best of them, bring the four together with flashing talent.

are low-key and the subtle brushwork is completely seductive.

What is the development, the evolution, of the technique which culminates in this goose and the other classic Crowell pieces? How do these techniques change through time?

THE EARLY WORK

The 1975 Massachusetts Duck Stamp pintail and a group of similarly handled canvasbacks may be Crowell's first gunning decoys. Whether this turns out to be true or not, they share interesting features - the most striking of which is the amount of detail seen in the carving. Various feather groups, scapulas, flanks, etc. are set out in relief,then further defined at the edges by grooved cuts and fine rasp marks. These birds are also gouged out between the carved wings, although oddly, their flight feathers, primaries, are not cut out.

The superb canvasback preener is also gouged out between the wings, but unlike the birds above, its primaries are deeply carved, to the point where each is concave. The Peabody Museum preening black duck (catalogue number 10) shares this renowned Crowell detail, but it stands apart on several counts. The bird has a fully raised wing that is held in place by a separate piece of wood representing the forewing; it has an open beak and most unusual, it is hollow.

The first shorebirds were given similar attention. Several of the dust-jacket plovers (catalogue numbers 2-4) have relief carved wrists (the leading edge of the wing) plus deeply carved wingtip separation and primaries. An early peep decoy (catalogue number 1) has its tertials crisply chiseled out along with its flight feathers.

FIGURE 47. Preening Canvasback drake, catalogue number 12. Collection of Ted and Judy Harmon

Even the first miniatures, the 1901 Cunningham and Phillips sets (catalogue numbers 66-69) share this extra detail. A black duck has two added-on wingtips and a number of sandpipers have dropped carved wings.

Another striking feature about the early work is its sense of animation. The life-size Peabody Museum sandpiper (catalogue number 32) is caught midstride across its oyster shell , and it is calling back over its shoulder. In the 1901 miniature groups, many birds are shown mid-run, and a blue-wing teal (not in the exhibit) is open-beaked, quacking. The regal dust-jacket beetleheads create a powerful sense of motion when displayed together which is how they were designed to be seen. The same can be said of the 1908 black duck group (catalogue number 9); the decoys with chip-carved flanks. One swims forward, one loafs contentedly, a third tucks its head in sleep, a forth reaches well over its back, preening. (Not included in the exhibit) Such activity becomes rare in Crowell waterfowl; some of these poses are never seen again.

The early material also exhibits a wide variety of paintwork. The most intriguing is found on the dust-jacket plovers. On the underside each bird is shown in early fall molt the black is bold and forthright. The same is true of the paint on the primaries; in fact, here, thick bristle strokes literally become the feather barbs. The upper portion of these birds, however, is very different. The complicated saddle and wing plumage is done in a tentative, almost an exploratory, fashion: it is sketchy; and the two colors, black and grey, are applied so thinly that the primer is clearly visible beneath them. The overall impression is one of learning: these stately beetleheads truly look as though they were the first shorebirds Elmer Crowell ever made.

The Peabody Museum mantel sandpiper (catalogue number 32) shows a more certain touch, Like the other early work, the colors are limited to earth tones, but these are well used; the chest is dotted with four or five distinct

FIGURE 48. Spotted Sandpiper miniature, 1901, only 2 ½" long. Courtesy Philip DeNormandie.

hues, and the back is richly colored. The mantel and wing plumage is painstakingly drawn in paint rather than painted, but it is a confident rendering.

Curiously, the tiny ducks and shorebird decoys show the completely developed blending and stippling seen on their larger later counterparts. They are true miniatures of the finest Crowell birds.

Almost the complete range of brush-handling is present on the first life-sized waterfowl; the delicate facial shading, the blurred streaks and the softly pulled body feathers are all in place. The famous paint is coming into full flower.

A few of the pieces can be faulted to some degree as birds; the mantel sandpiper (cat. number 32) has a slightly froggy look head-on, as does the peep decoy (cat. number 1). The 1901 miniatures have some of the stilted look of mounts and illustrations of the day; in fact, they may have been inspired by these. The rotund miniature goldeneye's head is certainly small, but overall, these birds have charm and they would delight any naturalist. The duck and goose decoys are another thing; they are keenly observed and well presented.

**FIGURE 49 &
50.** Two views of
the dust-jacket
plovers. Courtesy
Ted and Judy
Harmon.

THE OVAL BRAND

The best of the branded decoys - those made for Cunningham, Phillips and others - are masterful in all respects. The ducks are sensitively portrayed; most are relaxed, but alert, and they have turned heads; they look right at the viewer. Some have a sassy expression, an impudence that is beguiling. The knifework on these pieces is sure and clean; most birds have sharply carved wingtips, tail and beak. The paint is magnificent; all colors are used, but they are muted, and the blended brushwork is so varied and subtle that it is difficult to follow. The overwhelming impression, when looking at these birds, is that meticulous care was taken with each.

The standard gunning blocks of this period are finished in a more straight-forward manner. The decoys are generally sturdier, thicker tailed - they look like working birds. The carving is efficient, spare - there is little extra detail - and the paint- handling is streamlined. The birds carry quickly-pounced shading on flank and back rather than the more time-consuming blended brush strokes, and the colors are brighter. This is not to take away from the birds; they are well done and they are convincing decoys.

The shorebird decoys, too, have been pared down to essentials. The carved feathering is gone - though the separation between wing and tail remains to the end. The paint has become a swift shorthand for plumage; it is rendered in blended strokes, dabs and spots. It shows a glimpse of plover, of wader - and certainly no more than this was needed for the decoy to do its work. These birds were effective; buckshot holes bear silent testimony to it.

The oval-branded mantel birds are fascinating, both in themselves of course, but also because they so clearly demonstrate the Crowell's progression from decoy-makers to decorative carvers. The earliest of the shorebirds look like decoys mounted on bases. The paint work and somewhat drab colors illustrate overall pattern rather than actual plumage, and the birds are simple in form. At some point, however, a change occurs, and the birds begin to look as though they are done from study-skins or specimens. Feather groups, the secondaries and their coverts, appear on the wing, and the painting itself becomes rich and feathery. The colors have a snap. The birds are lively, more accurate and far more detailed. The personalized carvings, again, made for Hardy and other friends, are outstanding portraits of the species they depict, particularly for their era. They are unmatched.

The same transition can be spotted in the miniatures. The birds in the early groups look like scaled-down decoys; they are slender, racy-looking and a little rough in finish - the bandsaw kerf is visible beneath their tails and throats. The almost perfunctory paint is quickly brushed on in a series of slashes and specks. The colors - some of which look as if they came straight from the tube - appear bright because they are applied thinly, like glazes, over white primer. The birds belly holes are unfilled.

The later sets look as though more time was devoted to them. the birds are sanded, the colors are mixed and toned down and the paint is lush - it is put in place by a sure hand. Each feather group is understood and clearly delineated, then further defined with finely modulated shading or blending. Strangely, these models are broad of beam, particularly across the wingtips they no longer taper toward the tail like their predecessors and the living bird. All belly holes are now filled.

FIGURE 51. Miniature Yellowlegs, c. 1910. Note the rough kerf under the tail feathers. This bird is only 3½ inches long. Heritage Plantation Collection

FIGURE 52. Miniature Hudsonian Godwit, c. 1915-1928. This is a later miniature with clearly delineated feather groups. The paint is thickly applied with precision. This bird is 5¼ inches long. Collection of Philip DeNormandie.

THE RECTANGULAR IMPRESSION

The carvings bearing this mark look like decorative pieces. Some of the birds strike inventive poses, like the yellowlegs preening its lifted wing (catalogue number 35). The wing, of course, provides a grand canvas for paint - and the paint of this period is done in an effortless manner. The colors run the gamut from softly delicate to bright and intense, almost harsh, depending on the decoy or the type of bird being done. A wider range of quality is seen in this work; some of it is very fine, but some is done hurriedly, with less care. There are occasional mistakes: a mantel quail and woodcock tower over their shelfmates on 3-inch high wader legs, and a few Bob White lack the black and white barring on the chest and belly that helps identify the species. Overall, however, the promise of the Crowell name is kept, and the birds have all the realism, grace and form one could hope for.

GLOSSARY

THE BASIC STEPS OF BIRD CARVING

A detailed drawing of a bird is done in profile from reference material or fieldwork. The outline of the drawing is transferred from paper onto a piece of cardboard and then cut out, leaving a positive cardboard pattern. The pattern is placed on a prepared block of wood and traced around like a stencil, then the finished outline is bandsawed out of the block. This produces a blank, an exact wooden sideview of the bird. The blank now has the bird's top view drawn onto its top surface - this is done either freehand or with a top-view pattern - and this, too, is bandsawed out. The resulting squarish bird is rounded off with a chisel, drawknife or blade. When it has been taken down to its final dimensions, the details are carved in and the piece is sanded, primed and painted.

PAINTING TERMS

Blending refers to layering down two or more colors next to, or over, one another, then sweeping them lightly with a soft, clean brush while they are wet. This blurs and softens the paint colors.

Stippling or pouncing is done with a stiff flat-bottomed brush. Paint is picked up on the bristle ends with a delicate, vertical stabbing motion, then it is applied using the same action. The technique leaves and even, pebbly, speckled appearance, and can be used to cover large amounts of surface quickly.

PLATE I

PLATE II

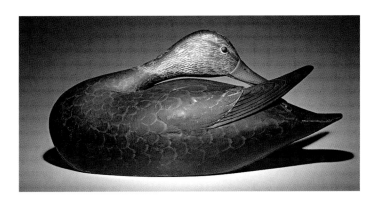

PLATE III

PLATE IV

PLATE V

PLATE VI

PLATE VII

PLATE VIII

PLATE IX

PLATE X

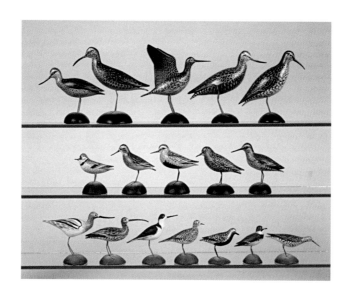

PLATE XI

PLATE XII

THE CATALOGUE

By Brian Cullity

Note: dating Crowell carvings has always been somewhat of an arbitrary and futile business. At least three different rubber stamps, two brands and a paper label were used in signing various carvings from the shop. Additionally, both Elmer and Cleon would often sign and date a work in pen and ink, especially in the later years. The prolific use of the various marks and signatures undoubtedly contributed to the success of the business. The vast majority of all the carvings made after about 1912

other reasons, including whim, influenced whether or not brands or marks were added to any given carving or decoy.

Three different rubber stamps were used in the Crowell workshop. These were used to apply ink signatures to the bases of the carvings, primarily the miniatures. They are often quite faded and difficult to see. They all date from the earliest period of Crowell's professional carving but were in continuous use throughout the careers of both Elmer and Cleon.

FIGURE 53. Oval ink mark. This mark is rarely seen. This example was stamped in one of Elmer's books.

FIGURE 54. "Maker" ink mark. This is on the base of a miniature Bluebird. Collection of Steve Tyng.

FIGURE 55. "MFR" ink mark. This is quite faint, as is often the case with the ink stamps. "Golden-eye" and "Male" are written in pencil in Cleon's hand. The species were often identified on the base. Collection of Jackson Parker.

bear some sort of mark. This was a brilliant marketing ploy which paid off handsomely. The various marks can be very misleading, however, if used as tools for dating a carving. Not all carvings were signed after 1912. Not all brands and labels were used sequentially and an early "MAKER" mark might be found on a relatively late bird. The best approach is to consider the object itself.

The lack of the oval brand does not date the decoy before 1912. Many were made after that date without any mark. A practical consideration helps explain this fact. The brand had to be heated in the pot-bellied stove before being applied to the base of the decoy. A roaring fire in a stove, in a very small workshop, in the middle of a hot summer day is not a practical method of working. Surely

The circular "Maker" mark is found on all the carvings made for the Robert Scott family of Osterville and now in the Heritage Plantation collection. Family history recalls that these were commissioned in the fall of 1908 and delivered in 1909 or 1910. These marks are most often found on what are considered to be the earliest miniatures. It is also known for a fact that Cleon, on at least one occasion, marked a carving with the "Maker" mark and the oval ink stamp as late as c.1955. (see catalogue number 74) The presence of these ink marks should, therefore, be taken cautiously. It is believed that the various ink stamps were used very infrequently after the rectangular brand was made. From a practical standpoint, the rectangular impression was far

FIGURE 56. An early impression of the oval brand. This is on a rectangular base of a decorative that was owned by Dr. Cunningham. All Cunningham birds were marked by the owner with three small holes drilled into the bottom. Courtesy Steve Tyng, Pleasant Bay Antiques.

easier to use and didn't fade.

The oval brand measuring 3⅛ inches by 1⅞ inches was made between 1910-1915, most likely 1912. Dr. George Ross Starr, Jr. relates that Crowell told him he "had his now-famous brand made in 1915, and that all decoys from then on were marked with it." (pp156-157) However, the Great Blue Heron in the collection of Shelburne Museum bears the oval brand and the date 1912 (see figure 20).

It is reasonable to assume that Crowell had the brand made in 1912, the first year of his business. It is especially revealing that this dated example is a presentation piece to Mrs. Charles Ashley Hardy, whose husband reportedly

FIGURE 57. A very late impression of the oval brand, c. 1928. Note how the outer rim has almost disappeared. It is entirely missing from later strikes.

established Crowell in his profession.

It also appears that the brand had a definite lifespan. The oval, probably made from iron, was made to be heated and then burned into the base of a carving. A number of decoys have what appear to be crudely made copies of the brand, yet a closer examination reveals that the oval brand had begun to disintegrate - affecting the quality of the lettering and eroding the outside line until it disappears completely. One of these late strikes can be seen on the wall of the workshop today.

The brand continued to be used for special requests such as on the Ruddy duck decoy illustrated in catalogue number 20. However, it was replaced by the rectangular impression, for all practical purposes, during the 1920's.

It was becoming apparent that a hotter strike and harder blow were necessary to make the desired impression with the oval brand. The obvious solution was to have a new brand made - the rectangular stamp found on most later carvings. Oral tradition from a number of collectors and dealers has dated that stamp from 1928 and indeed, it is believed that the oval brand survived about fifteen years before wearing out. That would date the beginning of the rectangular stamp to about 1927-1928. An article in The Cape Cod Magazine in 1951 states that Crowell decoys "may still be identified because they were all branded with a square stamp that was in use for 15 years." The author was undoubtedly referring to the oval brand and the reference to the rectangular form was an error.

Another substantiating fact is recorded in the order book for the years 1927-1928. Henry A. Evers Co., 21 Eddy Street, Providence is written on a page and "Brands" is jotted next to the name. It turns out that the Evers Company is still in business and they make steel dies and stamps, specializing in logos and company names. Unfortunately, they related that their records for the years 1925-1930 do not exist; however, the evidence clearly indicates that the workshop had the rectangular impression made in 1927 or 1928.

For the purposes of this show, the dates for the oval are all c. 1912-1928. A disintegrating brand would place a particular carving towards the later years. There is, also, always the possibility that a special request would be made in later years to apply the oval such as seen on the Ruddy Duck. The benefit of doubt will be given for the rectangular impression and the beginning date for that will be 1925 for this catalogue.

It is known that the rectangular stamp was used continuously from its inception until Cleon's death in 1961. This impression was formed without the benefit of heating and only required a blow with the hammer to make the impression. A few examples are known to have been inked at the time of striking the impression. Two theories exist concerning the implementation of the blue

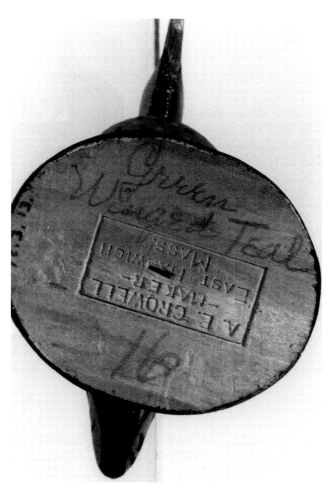

FIGURE 58. A typical impression made with the rectangular stamp. The handwriting is Cleon's. Note the elongated hole in the wood. All miniature Crowell carvings have this type of hole on the base and on the bellies of the bird. The carvings were stuck on a metal shaft while they were being painted.

A.E. CROWELL & SON
Bird
Carving
E. HARWICH, MASS.

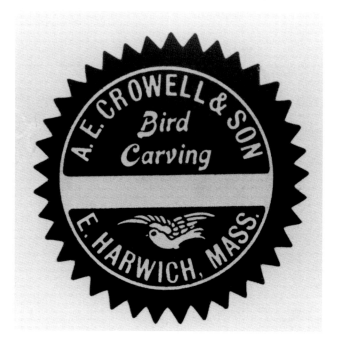

FIGURE 59. The blue paper label.

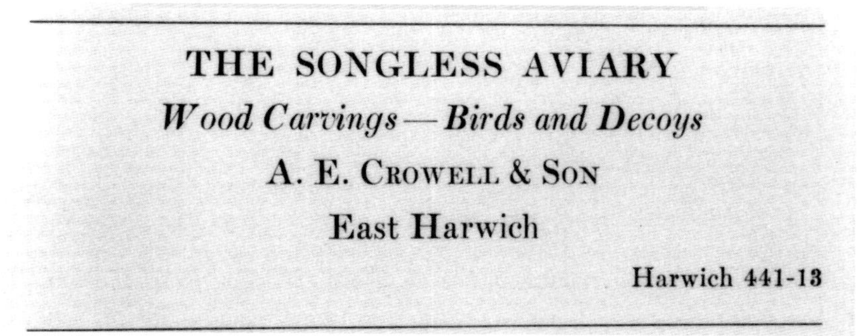

THE SONGLESS AVIARY
Wood Carvings—Birds and Decoys
A. E. Crowell & Son
East Harwich
Harwich 441-13

FIGURE 60. Advertisement placed in 1936 by A.E. Crowell & Son in "About Cape Cod" by Joe Lincoln.

FIGURE 61. A typical pen and ink signature of Elmer's. This is on the bottom of the miniature Mallard Duck, catalogue number 73.

paper label. This label bears the legend "A.E. Crowell & Son/Bird Carving" along with a space for writing the name of the species of the bird. The label had a glued back to allow it to be applied to the bottom of the carvings.

The first theory suggests that it was made to recognize the return of Cleon to the business in 1920. Indeed, a number of carvings suggest this possibility. A group of Crowell decoratives was sold at auction in 1987 with a history of having been purchased from Crowell during the 1920's. They all bear the blue paper label. (Guyette, lots 715A-715H, 9/19/87) The same auction had a decorative duck with both the oval brand and paper label (lot 397) which, again, would suggest a date in the 1920's.

The second theory suggests that the label was the last mark used, since it is the only one acknowledging the role of Cleon in the business. This is assuming the rectangular impression dates from c. 1925-1928. The first printed reference to A.E. Crowell & Son, found to date, is an advertisement in a 1936 publication by Joseph C. Lincoln (the author).

This is the same advertisement in which the title "The Songless Aviary" is first used. The addition of "& Son" to the firm could have signaled the increasingly important role Cleon was playing by the mid-thirties. Regardless of the date, the paper label was a problem to use. It often fell off the carving and was more difficult to use than the rectangular impression. Cleon, however, did continue to use this label occasionally his entire career (see catalogue number 81).

Most of Elmer's handwritten signatures date from the mid thirties through 1943, although several are known from the early years of the business. Often, these are found on presentation carvings such as the Small-Mouth Bass he made and presented to his friend Joseph C. Lincoln, the author, in 1917 (Sold at the Richard A, Bourne sale of March 7, 1987, lot 128). Cleon started signing his own name and using his Harwichport address after his father stopped working. These works can all be dated from after 1946 when Cleon moved to that village. Cleon retained the Harwichport address for the remainder of his life. Some of these are signed "C.S. Crowell, Harwichport" and others are signed "A.E. Crowell & Son, Harwichport." Both indicate that they were made by Cleon, after 1946.

Again, regardless of the mark or signature, the first and foremost consideration should be the quality of the carving and painting. A lifetime of work will have both good and bad examples and should be judged accordingly. Cleon, at his best, was a superb carver and painter and should be accorded that acknowledgment. As can be seen, the dates are a matter of speculation and logic made without hard facts. The presence, or lack of, any given mark or brand should be regarded as useful information towards attribution, and only cautiously as a marker of age.

FIGURE 62. Pen and ink signature by Cleon Crowell, c. 1946-1961. This is on the bottom of catalogue number 42.

DECOYS

The best decoys made in the Crowell shop are those done by Elmer in the earliest years. They show a degree of love, labor and artistic supremacy unmatched in the later work. The level of skill and art was readily acknowledged, even at that early date, and many of these fine birds never saw the water. In many respects it is a matter of speculation whether or not certain birds are decoys or ornamental carvings. We do know of shorebirds, for instance, that were made as decoys and then mounted as ornamentals with two legs. (The opposite is also true and collectors should be aware of ornamentals that have been altered to appear as working decoys) All full sized, unmounted carvings are presented as such and determination of original use is not generally speculated on in this catalogue. Notations are made when an owner or a history is known.

SHOREBIRD DECOYS

The earliest of Elmer Crowell's shorebird decoys are categorically some of the finest folk sculptures created. Few were made by his son, Cleon, as the gunning laws had ended most shorebird hunting by the time he started working full time in the shop in 1920, although at least one order for a Yellowlegs decoy was made around 1928. The one example in the show known to have been made by Cleon was purchased from his widow. She related, at the time of purchase, that Cleon made two of these "because he had really never made very many shorebird decoys."

The first Crowell shorebirds have painted brass tack eyes, as do the early ornamental shorebirds. Black glass eyes imported from England soon replaced tacks; and later, paperweight eyes replaced the black glass. An entry in the order books for 1930 mentions a purchase of these eyes: "7 doz hazel/ 50 pair of yellow straw/150 pair hazel" and "get 12 pair for Theodore, hazel." These observations are a rule of thumb and not meant to be taken as an absolute chronology. Exceptions have been noted, especially with the use of painted tack eyes in later carvings.

1. SANDPIPER

Color Illustration PLATE I
Before 1918
H. 2¾ L. 6
Courtesy Ted and Judy Harmon

The brass tack eyes, finely carved wings and tail feathers and chip carved back are all indications of a very early date on this sandpiper or "peep." It is most likely a Semipalmated or Least Sandpiper and is a working decoy although x-ray examination does not reveal any lead shot. Note the manner in which the head is turned ever so slightly to obtain a most life-like appearance. This was carved from a single block of wood.

2. STANDING BLACK - BELLIED PLOVER
Color Illustration PLATE II
Before 1918
H. 6¼ L. 12
Courtesy Ted and Judy Harmon

This plover and the following two are from the group of so-called "dust-jacket" birds illustrated on the cover of William Mackey's book "American Bird Decoys." They are three supreme creations of Elmer Crowell and represent the finest in decoy carving and painting. The deeply carved feathers and boldly sculpted bodies are finished with blended painted feather patterns, unique to the Crowell hand. These birds come from at least two different gunning rigs and differ slightly from each other in carving technique.

The Black-Bellied Plover, or beetle-head as Crowell and other hunters referred to them, is really mis-named. The black extends only to the thigh. The Golden Plover is the real black-bellied bird. Beetle-heads were very gun shy and great care was taken to create realistic decoys to attract them to a stand. This and the following two examples were found on the North Shore.

3. BLACK-BELLIED PLOVER   Color Illustration PLATE II
Before 1918
H. 6 L. 11
Courtesy Ted and Judy Harmon

This plover is in the feeding position and is stamped with the name "G. W. Loud" under the tail. Loud was probably the name of the owner of the rig. If these were purchased from Elmer by Loud, then they would date after 1900 as Crowell did not sell any decoys prior to that date. The black glass eyes are also an indication that they were made by Crowell after he became a professional carver.

4. BLACK-BELLIED PLOVER   Color Illustration PLATE II
Before 1918
H. 6 L. 9
Courtesy Ted and Judy Harmon

The realistically cocked head position is classic Crowell. This bird differs from the previous two in the treatment of the tail feather carving and also lacks the subtly carved shoulder. The paint is superb.

5. PAIR OF YELLOWLEGS
Color Illustration PLATE I
Before 1928
H. 5 L. 11 and 12
Courtesy Ted and Judy Harmon

This pair of Yellowlegs was found in New Hampshire and appears to be quite early. It is believed that the black glass eyes, as seen here, were used by Elmer before the paperweight eyes. X-rays reveal that the black glass eyes were attached by a metal pin as opposed to the cementing used for the paperweight eyes. The x-ray also revealed that the bill of the longer bird was attached by means of a very finely whittled wooden peg. Again, note the subtle turn to the head and the laboriously carved wing and tail feathers. These features are all indicative of a rather early date.

6. LESSER YELLOWLEGS
Before 1918
H. 3¾ L. 8¾
Courtesy Ted and Judy Harmon

The Lesser Yellowlegs was a relatively uncommon species to be used as a model for a decoy . This example has the early brass tack eyes, plain painted surface with no carved details. The holes in the body are from lead shot and are characteristic of working decoys.

7. GOLDEN PLOVER
Before 1918
H. 3 L. 12
Courtesy Ted and Judy Harmon

This bird is in the running position and has the early black glass eyes, carved wing tips and a slightly downward curved tail. Golden Plover decoys by the elder Crowell are quite scarce. He once related that "Golden Plover were not plentiful in my time, although I have shot quite a few."

8. BLACK-BELLIED PLOVER
Cleon Crowell
c. 1955-1960
H. 4½ L. 9½
Courtesy Mr. Donald B. Howes

It was related that Cleon made this and another shorebird for himself for sentimental reasons shortly before his death. It is not the best carving or painting and was probably done in haste. The eyes were placed asymmetrically, the body is very heavy and the painting leaves much to be desired. Cleon did not always work up to his capabilities, especially in his later years. His deteriorating health may have contributed to that factor.

DUCK DECOYS

The few ducks known with so-called chipped carved bodies are some of Elmer Crowell's earliest efforts. One example is known to have been made by him as a wedding gift about the year 1908. It is illustrated in John Delph's book, "New England Decoys."

The head on the sleeper of this group is attached with two square nails and has paperweight eyes. It is a working decoy (as are the other two) and has some lead shot in the body. The chip carved surface was a purposeful technique that was labor intensive. The bodies of these three birds are larger than later Black Ducks and have a very pronounced breast. Crowell stated in a 1914 interview that his philosophy was to make each duck (in a rig) in a different position for the sake of realism. The three shown here represent a sleeper, a swimmer and a contented duck (the head is tucked down)

9. THREE BLACK DUCKS
1900-1910
H. 6 L. 17
Courtesy Ted and Judy Harmon

10. BLACK DUCK Color Illustration PLATE III

c. 1900-1915
H. 7¼ L. 16
Courtesy The Peabody Museum of Salem, photograph by
Mark Sexton

This is one of Elmer Crowell's masterpieces made for his
friend and employer, Dr. John C. Phillips of Beverly and
Boston. It is marked on the bottom with the initials "JCP"
and descended in the Phillips family until it was donated to
the Peabody Museum. Crowell made a number of very
special decoys and carvings for a few close associates early in
this century. He was obviously producing the finest examples
his hands could create and they stand today as some of the
greatest carvings of the decoy world. Few examples can
match this in grace, form, paint or balance.

The preening head and raised wing tip are attached with
nails, as is the bottom.

11. BLACK DUCK

c. 1912-1913
H. 6½ L. 17 ¼
Courtesy The Shelburne Museum,
photograph by Ken Burns.

This is one of the Black Ducks
Crowell made for the Iver Johnson
sporting goods store in Boston.
Mackey reported that Crowell made
ten dozen a year for two years, but
they were not very successful sellers.
These were made in the very first
years of Crowell's business and
demonstrate a mature and
sophisticated form and paint
application. They differ considerably
from the earlier chip carved bodies.
Unlike most Crowell decoys which
are made from white pine, this
example is made from cedar.

Crowell marked all these Black Ducks
with a stencil bearing the "Iver
Johnson" name and "Supreme" in
white paint.

12. CANVASBACK DRAKE   Color Illustration PLATE IV

c. 1912
H. 7 L. 15
Courtesy Ted and Judy Harmon

The unpainted base of this magnificent preening Canvasback is signed in pencil "A. Elmer Crowell/East Harwich/Mass./"MFR"". The term "manufacturer" and the "MFR" mark start appearing around 1912. Crowell began carving full time in that year and the town of Harwich started to tax him for "machinery used in manufacturing" decoys. It is quite likely that Crowell made this about that time, but before he had his oval brand made.

This has the rarely seen chip carving between the wing tips and fully carved details of the wings and tail. The head is attached with two square nails at the body and one square nail through the neck. No dowel was used. Very bright paperweight eyes are present. The carving is carefully executed and superb. No other preening Canvasbacks are known and even regular Canvasbacks by Crowell are quite scarce. Canvasback Ducks, are rarely seen in New England; however, they were common in the Chesapeake Bay region.

13. REDHEAD DRAKE

c. 1910
H. 7½ L.15½
Heritage Plantation collection (1972.3.2)

It is believed that this Redhead came from the same rig on Martha's Vineyard as the pair illustrated in Starr's book (p. 157) and was purchased from Elmer Crowell in 1910. This and the mate (not shown) were from the Prescott Fay collection as are another pair now owned by the Dukes County Historical Society. Early features include fully carved primary feathers and tail, subtly blended paint and slightly oversized body. The tail on earlier ducks is often small and delicate with subtly curved feathers.

14. PAIR REDHEAD DUCKS   Color Illustration PLATE VII

1912-1928
H. 7½ L. 16½
Courtesy Ted and Judy Harmon

These are early oversized decoys with painted bottoms and the oval brand. Some decoys from the Crowell workshop were branded before the bases were painted and then an oval, metal plaque was attached with two brads. The body was then painted. Most of these metal plates have been removed over time and the result is a painted base with an unpainted oval brand. In other instances they just painted around the brand.

This pair of Redheads is in marvelous condition and has great paint, form and carved details. The painted surfaces are thickly applied and wonderfully blended. These are examples of the best quality Crowell working decoys.

15. REDHEAD DRAKE

c. 1920-1940
H. 7 L. 15½
Heritage Plantation Collection (1972.3.1)

This Redhead has a completely different method of paint application than the previous examples. The paint appears to have been pounced onto the body with the end of the brush, giving a very different appearance than seen on earlier examples. It probably represents a quicker method of painting. This technique is also seen on the Pintail (catalogue number 25) and Mallard Duck (catalogue number 24) in the show and is believed to be a later style than that seen on the decoys with fully carved primaries. Although this one does not have any mark, others with the same technique bear the rectangular stamp and one has both the rectangle and the oval.

The squarish, fluted tail carving also appears to be a later and slightly cruder method than seen on the earlier Redheads.

16. PAIR RED-BREASTED MERGANSER DUCKS

c. 1910-1920
H. 6¼ L. 17
Courtesy Ted and Judy Harmon

These great mergansers are from the Hinsdale rig from Mattapoisett which is located on Buzzards Bay. Although not marked with any Crowell brands, they probably date from 1910-1920. The paint on the drake's body is remarkably similar to that on the miniature merganser which dates from 1910 (catalogue number 76). These racy looking birds have both heads turned slightly for a more natural look. Elmer is often pictured with similar merganser decoys in the setting (see figures 23 & 25).

17. FEMALE WIDGEON
c. 1912-1928
H. 7 L. 15
Courtesy Ted and Judy Harmon

This scarce decoy has the rasped head and breast, oval brand and carefully blended and applied paint. No carving appears on the wings, however. This is another example of a decoy made from cedar, an unusual departure for the Crowell shop.

18. WOOD DUCK   Color Illustration PLATE V
c. 1912-1915
H. 6 L. 14
Courtesy Ted and Judy Harmon

This bird is from the Dr. John H. Cunningham collection. Cunningham was a hunting partner of Dr. Phillips and spent many days at the Wenham stand when Elmer Crowell was the gunning Captain. Consequently, Cunningham became closely acquainted with Crowell and became one of his first customers. The carvings from his collection (all of which were sold several years ago) bear the same care and talent exhibited on the Phillips' birds. Carvings from the Cunningham collection can be identified by the three small holes drilled into the bottoms of the pieces.

This example has the oval brand on a carefully prepared, sanded bottom. It is a superb decoy with carved and painted features that are difficult to surpass. Crowell has even captured the subtle V shaped markings on the breast. These carvings, made for Crowell's closest friends, are the best of his work.

19. RUDDY DUCK DRAKE
c. 1912-1915
H. 4¾ L. 10½
Courtesy Ted and Judy Harmon

This Ruddy Duck was made for Dr. John C. Phillips and is marked "JCP" on the unpainted base next to the oval brand. It is painted in the summer plumage and has the carved wing tips and tail feathers found on the finest examples by Elmer.

20. RUDDY DUCK
c. 1960-1961
H. 4 L. 10¼
Heritage Plantation Collection (1970.5.8)

This Ruddy, in marked contrast to the preceding example, is a later carving of marginal quality. It bears the oval brand in the later disintegrated state on a rough sawn , unpainted bottom. An entry in one of the order books covering the years 1960-1961 probably lists this very decoy: "1 life size ruddy duck decoy $35.00, old stamp branded in." This bird is shown in winter plumage with the characteristic "cocked" tail.

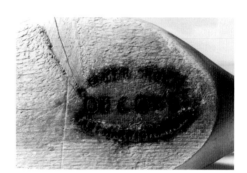

21. GOLDENEYE HEN
c.1912-1915
H. 5½ L. 12⅜
Courtesy Ted and Judy Harmon

This is another fine example from the Phillips Collection bearing the oval brand on an unpainted bottom. The tucked head position is meant to imitate a contented duck. It is assumed that all of the special carvings made for Dr. Phillips, Dr. Cunningham and Charles Hardy were produced by Elmer.

22. MALLARD HEN
C. 1912-1915
H. 6½ L. 15½
Courtesy Ted and Judy
Harmon

This Mallard hen from the
Phillips Collection exhibits all
of the finest details one would
expect on Crowell's best
carvings down to the most
minute painted features along
the bill. The carving is crisp
and sharp and the paint
exquisitely applied and
blended. This also bears the
oval brand.

23. MALLARD HEN
c. 1912-1925
H. 7 L. 16
Courtesy Jackson and Vivian
Parker

Very few cork body decoys
were produced in the Crowell
workshop. This one is branded
with the owner's name "F.
Winthrop" and the oval mark.
Note the effort made in
carving the features of the bill,
even though this was a lower
grade decoy.

24. MALLARD DRAKE
After 1925
H. 7¼ W. 17¼
Courtesy Ted and Judy Harmon

This fine mallard bears the rectangular stamp on an unpainted base. The workmanship is very good but reflects the increasing demands of the orders pouring into the workshop as the Crowell name becomes more famous. The wing tips are only outlined by carving, although the tail feathers continue to be sculpted as always. The head and breast are rasped and the paint is superb but displays less blending than seen on earlier examples. The body is more streamlined than a real mallard.

25. PINTAIL DRAKE
after 1925
H. 6¾ L. 17¼
Courtesy Donald Howes

Both the rectangular impression and the oval brand were used to mark the unpainted bottom of this Pintail drake. There is very little evidence of the blended feather patterns employed during the earlier years, although the form and paint are still superb.

26. SCAUP DRAKE
c.1912-1925
H. 6¼ L. 14
Anonymous Loan

Although darkened from use, this bird has spectacular paint. It was a gift to Elmer's very good friend and fellow hunter, Alfred B. Gardner of Accord. The head and bill are especially noteworthy for the superbly sculpted details. The plumage is that of an immature drake. Interestingly, the base of this duck is painted except for an oval where the brand would normally be placed; however, it was never marked.

27. PAIR SCAUP DUCKS
c.1915-1930
H. 6½ W. 14
Courtesy Ted and Alotta Whitney

Scaup are commonly called bluebills. This pair of unmarked decoys has the name "Dr. L. C. Jones" written in pencil on the painted bottom. These ducks, which lack most carved details or even the rasped head, represent the lower grade of gunning decoys made in the Crowell workshop. Even so, the paint is beautifully applied with some blending and the overall form is excellent.

28. SCAUP DRAKE
c. 1920-1935
H. 5½ L. 13¼
Heritage Plantation Collection (1972.3.3)

This is a regular grade working bluebill decoy. It has minimum carved tailfeathers and a rasped head and breast. The paint is nice, but not spectacular, especially when compared with figure 26.

29. PAIR GREEN-WING TEALS
After 1925
H. 5½ L. 12½ (male)
Heritage Plantation Collection (1970.5.9 & 1970.5.10)

This male teal has striking differences with figure 30, which was made by Cleon Crowell. This pair is branded with the rectangular stamp and has painted bottoms. The heads have been carved with the slight concavity that is found in nature. The bodies are slightly undersized.

30. GREEN WING TEAL

Cleon Crowell
c.1944-1960
H. 5⅛ L. 12⅜
Courtesy Donald Howes

Cleon kept this teal for many years before agreeing to part with it. It has been stamped with the rectangular brand and is signed in pen by Cleon. It is markedly different from the previous example. The head does not have the refined characteristics found on the better grade decoys and the body is slightly heavier. It does have the carved tail feathers, however. X-rays revealed that the interior construction is the same as earlier birds with the head attached by two angled nails.

Cleon continued making a limited number of decoys until his death in 1961. He favored Mallards, Pintails and Green Wing Teal.

31. CANADA GOOSE
c. 1912-1925
H. 12¼ L. 23
Courtesy Ted and Judy Harmon

This is one of three Canada Goose decoys found wrapped in newspaper in the Worcester area. It bears the oval brand and has tack eyes. The head and breast are heavily rasped and the paint is exceptional. Relatively few Canada Goose decoys were made in the workshop, probably because hunters in this area favored the use of live decoys until they were outlawed in 1935.

An early pattern for goose decoys, in the collection of Heritage Plantation, was made from a calendar dated 1905. Numerous notes in Elmer's hand cover the pattern and record the various dimensions, colors and the original order of three dozen decoys for a Mr. T. C. Howes of Connecticut. The pattern and the dimensions match this decoy. Crowell used only four colors to achieve his spectacular goose feather patterns: white, burnt sienna, red umber and black.

ORNAMENTAL CARVINGS

Elmer Crowell's best and earliest ornamental carvings were equal in quality to his decoys. Many of these examples were made for his favored customers and some were given as gifts. (The Charles Ashley Hardy family owned many of the early examples, and family history relates that most were gifts from Crowell. Since gentlemen did not generally give gifts to each other they were presented to Mrs. Hardy.) As with the decoys, the earliest life size ornamentals had fully carved primaries and tail feathers and the earliest style of paint. Later carvings show signs of less careful modeling and faster painting techniques.

LIFE SIZE ORNAMENTALS

Life size ornamental or "mantel" carvings were made in the Crowell workshop from the earliest years. The first were essentially decoys which were mounted on plain square bases with realistic legs. The bases had chamfered edges and were painted black. These plain bases were soon replaced with carved mounts resembling rocks or clam shells. The very best had detailed ridges and markings carefully carved and painted onto the surfaces. The earliest examples tended to have the paint thickly daubed onto the surface. Later mantel carvings display less concern with carved features and the painted surfaces are somewhat careless. The earlier, bold geometric painted feathers are replaced with more realistic patterning which loses the soft feel of the earlier carvings.

The later bases are often in the form of stained, chip carved mounds. These are probably Cleon's creations. The order books covering the period 1950-1961 often have references to "my base" and handwritten instructions for staining pine are found in the back of the 1952 book.

32. SANDPIPER
c.1900-1915
H. 5¼ L. 5¼
Courtesy The Peabody Museum of Salem, photograph by Mark Sexton

This is another carving made for Dr. John C. Phillips and carries the "JCP" mark on the underside of the shell. A very unusual, if not unique, feature is the use of a real oyster shell for the base. The stance, open beak, wonderful paint and real shell mount make this one of the most outstanding examples from the early years.

33. YELLOWLEGS   Color Illustration PLATE I
1912-1925
H. 10¾ L. 11
Heritage Plantation Collection (1972.3.41)

The style, color and application of paint on this mantel carving are
essentially the same as is found on Elmer Crowell's best shorebird decoys.
This is branded with the oval mark and has black glass eyes. The carved wing
tips are an especially fine detail found on the earliest and best quality birds.
The carved clamshell mount is also a most difficult achievement and rarely
seen.

34. YELLOWLEGS
1912-1925
H. 9½ L. 13¼
Anonymous Loan

The running Yellowlegs was often used as a decoy position, but is not found
as frequently as an ornamental. This particular example was a gift from Elmer
Crowell to his good friend Fred Gardner of Accord. It has the same clamshell
base as found on catalogue number 33 but lacks the carved wingtips. The oval
brand was used to sign the bottom. The eyes are either painted wood or metal
tacks instead of glass. The beak on this example has been broken and mended
in the past making it somewhat shorter than it should be.

35. PREENING YELLOWLEGS
c. 1925-1940
H. 13½ L. 8
Heritage Plantation Collection (1969.1.5)

This Yellowlegs has a reduced amount of carving on the tail feathers and the simpler rounded base found on many of the Crowell ornamentals. It bears the rectangular brand on the bottom of the mount. The preening shorebird was a superb creation of the Crowell shop and was also made in a smaller version. The order books reveal that most preening birds were made during the 1930's and were referred to as "wing up" models. They cost $35.00 while a regular Yellowlegs cost $25.00.

36. FEEDING YELLOWLEGS
1941
H. 7½ L. 8½
Heritage Plantation Collection (1969.1.4)

Here, a later example sports a simplified painted clamshell base rather than the carved example in figure 32. The bottom of the base is signed with the rectangular brand and also in pen and ink: "A.E. Crowell/Maker/Cape Cod/1941" in Elmer's handwriting.

37. FEEDING LESSER YELLOWLEGS
c. 1925-1943
H. 7¼ L. 7¼
Heritage Plantation Collection (1972.3.10)

This example of a Lesser Yellowlegs is branded with the rectangular mark and signed in ink "A.E. Crowell" in Elmer's handwriting. Below that, in Cleon's printing, is "Yellowlegs." The carved oyster shell reveals a great degree of labor but the clumsy legs and rather poor quality paint job suggest that this is not one of their better efforts. The pattern for the oyster shell base is illustrated in catalogue number 161.

38. BLACK-BELLIED PLOVER
1932
H. 9¼ L. 8½
Courtesy Gigi Hopkins

The lender's father commissioned four carvings from the Crowell workshop in 1929 which were completed in 1932. This Black-bellied Plover or "beetlehead" and the Woodcock (figure 52) are two of those carvings. Crowell made numerous changes in the form of the Black-bellied Plover over the years. This example has a stouter neck and smaller body than the early shorebird decoys illustrated in figures 2-4. Various patterns indicate oversize, model, decoy, feeding, running and turned head variations of this popular bird. The paint on this example is more patterned and realistic than that of the earlier decoys, but still exhibits the exquisite blending found in the best of their works. It is unsigned.

39. COMMON SNIPE
c. 1912-1925
H. 7¾ L. 9½
Heritage Plantation Collection (1972.3.6)

This Common Snipe, also called a Wilson or Jack Snipe, is a superb example of the best ornamental carvings produced in the Crowell shop. Notice how even the slight overhang of the bill is captured in this exquisite carving. The eyes are painted, not glass, and the base bears the oval brand. The Crowells charged $25.00 for this size mantel carving from 1928-1933. Later, the price rose to $35.00.

40. COMMON SNIPE
After 1925
H. 7 L. 6
Heritage Plantation Collection (1970.5.4)

This is a later version of the snipe and features drop wings, painted tack eyes and the rectangular brand. The overall quality of the paint is quite good, but not as nice as the previous example. Notice the lack of carved detail on the bill compared to number 39. The paint lacks the flow and blending found on the earlier carving. The order books refer to this position as "wing down." They were not as expensive as the "wing up" birds.

41. PIPING PLOVER   Color Illustration PLATE IX
after 1925
H. 5¼ W. 5½
Heritage Plantation Collection (1973.75)

Piping Plovers are not mentioned in the order books until around the mid forties. This one appears earlier in form compared to the next example, but both are probably by Cleon. This example bears the the rectangular brand and "Piping Plover" written in pencil in Cleon's handwriting. The scooped tail and careful modeling of the head reveal a more carefully crafted example than that of number 42.

42. PIPING PLOVER   Color Illustration PLATE IX
Cleon Crowell
1946-1961
H. 5¼ L. 5
Heritage Plantation Collection (1972.3.9)

The bottom of this plover is signed in ink, "C.S. Crowell/Harwichport/Mass" (see figure 42) and stamped with the rectangular brand. Cleon lived in Harwichport from 1946 until his death in 1961, although he continued to work in the old workshop in East Harwich. His address prior to 1946 was always East Harwich according to tax records. It is therefore believed that all carvings bearing the Harwichport address were made by him after that date. Note the differences in modeling (especially the head) and in the paint application from the example in figure 41.

43. SANDPIPER

c. 1965-1970
H. 4⅜ L. 7½
Heritage Plantation Collection

This is a faked Crowell carving. The paint, form and eyes differ from any known example and the handwritten signature on the bottom, "A.E. Crowell/Maker/Cape Cod," appears to be a very poor attempt at imitating Elmer's distinctive writing. Other factors indicating a spurious origin include a stained bottom (over the signature) and the lack of the proper type mounting hole on both the base and the carving. All Crowell miniatures have a sharp oblong hole where they were mounted on dowels to hold them while being painted.

44. PREENING BLACK DUCK

c. 1912-1925
H. 10⅛ L. 14
Heritage Plantation Collection (1972.3.7)

Only a few of these graceful preening black duck mantel ornaments are known and they all vary to one degree or another. This particular one lacks the carved primaries found on the best examples, but has superb paint. The oval brand was used to sign the bottom of this fine carving. The preening position was one of the most graceful and successful forms used by the Crowells. The head and neck pattern for this bird is illustrated in catalogue number 124.

45. BLACK DUCK

c. 1925-1944
H. 8 L. 11½
Heritage Plantation Collection
(1970.5.11)

Carvings of this size are considered half or three-quarter models but are included here for lack of another category in which to place them. This one is marked with the rectangular brand and has the added ink inscription "A.E. Crowell/Cape Cod" in Elmer's handwriting on the base. The carving and paint are of a high quality including a rasped head and carved tail feathers.

46. WOOD DUCK   Color Illustration PLATE V

1912-1925
H. 10¾ L.16¾
Anonymous Loan

This superb Wood Duck has seven long carved primary wing feathers which meet in the middle of the back. The Cunningham example has fewer carved primaries and they are shorter and cross each other. Both were made during the same period, yet exhibit interesting differences. The paint also shows considerable variation from the Cunningham example. This model, mounted on a base, was made as a gift to Fred Gardner's brother-in-law, Ernest Loring, who was also a gunning friend of Elmer's. It is signed with the oval brand.

47. GREEN WING TEAL HEAD

c. 1924-1930
H. 1¼ L. 6
Courtesy Philip DeNormandie

Three patterns for "hissing" fowl were done by Elmer and two are dated 1924 (catalogue number 132). This head probably dates from around that period and may have been made for the J.J. Storrow hunting camp on Cape Cod, as was the Canada Goose in figure 48. This head is made from white pine, unlike most of the smaller carvings which were cedar. The eyes are painted brass tacks.

48. CANADA GOOSE HEAD

1924
H. 2¾ L. 8¾
Courtesy Albert and Judy Minucci

The pattern for this head is illustrated in catalogue number 132 and bears the penciled notation "Hat Hanger/Fancy/Storrow/Nov. 27, 1924" on the reverse. It is a superbly carved and painted head, even down to the "teeth" and under cut tongue. The eyes are brass tacks rather than the large black glass eyes found in earlier geese.

J.J. Storrow opened a hunting camp on a high bluff overlooking the northwest side of Long Pond in 1924. This hat hanger was most likely made for Storrow's camp. The Crowells also made a number of goose decoys for Storrow (catalogue number 134).

49. CANADA GOOSE HEAD

1912-1925
H. 6½ L. 13 (plaque)
Anonymous Loan

This half goose head is mounted on a stained pine plaque similar to the fish plaques. It was a gift to Fred Gardner from Elmer and is signed with the oval brand on the back. Black glass eyes are used instead of brass tacks. Crowell and Gardner were close friends and hunted geese together at Oldham Pond in Pembroke.

50. CANADA GOOSE   Color Illustration PLATE VI
1917
H. 15¼ W. 18¼ L. 36¼
Courtesy Albert and Judith Minucci

This full size goose was made for Harry V. Long in 1917 along with a preening goose, now in a western collection. The patterns for both are illustrated in catalogue numbers 98 and 99. The bottom of the base of this goose bears the oval brand. Harry V. Long was a businessman from Cohasset, Massachusetts, and ordered numerous carvings from the Crowell shop. The Brant pattern (catalogue number 101) is so similar in design and materials as to suggest that it, too, was made for Long at the same time, although it has no markings.

This is one of the supreme examples of Crowell carving and painting. It represents a hissing goose and has all the vitality and movement that one would expect from a live goose in a defensive position. The undulating neck, bold stance and threatening wings are a lively canvas for Crowell's talented brush.

51. PAIR OF BOBWHITE
c. 1912-1925
H. 7 W. 7½
Heritage Plantation Collection (1970.5.6 a &b)

Both of these Bobwhite bear the oval brand and "Robson/Fe. Quail" and "Robson/M Quail" in pencil in Elmer's handwriting. The unusually shaped base is an indication of early work as is the heavily daubed paint on the surface and the black glass eyes. Note the care taken to carve the details around the beak and the not so realistic spindly legs - both identifying characteristics of the Crowell workshop. A similar pair is known to have been made for Charles A. Hardy and have the carved primaries and similar bases. It is believed that the Hardy quail were made around 1912-1915 and this pair would date about the same time.

52. WOODCOCK
1932
H. 8 L. 10½
Courtesy Gigi Hopkins

This bird is another of the group that was commissioned in 1929 and delivered in 1932 (figure 38). The drop wing and perky uplifted and carved tail are but two of the fine details that went into this superb carving. Even the slight overhang at the tip of the bill is accurately captured along with beautifully applied and blended painted feathers. It is signed with the rectangular stamp.

53. RUFFED GROUSE
c. 1925-1943
H. 12 W. 10½
Heritage Plantation Collection (1970.5.6 a & b)

Upland game birds were not requested as often as ducks and shorebirds. They were more difficult to paint and were priced slightly higher. This example is signed with the rectangular impression and, interestingly, lacks the correct feather pattern on the breast.

54. KINGFISHER WITH PERCH
after 1925
H. 8 L. 10½
Courtesy Albert and Judith Minucci

The Kingfisher with a Perch in its beak was a popular carving and was made from the 1920's through 1960. They sold for $25.00 in 1930 and were mounted either on a branch or a rock base. This one bears the rectangular impression on the bottom.

55. PINE WARBLER

c. 1905-1920
H. 2½. W. 4½
Heritage Plantation Collection (1970.5.1)

This warbler was used as an ornament on a clock in the Elmer Crowell household until purchased by the Museum. It has carved wings and the distinctive paint found on the earliest carvings. Full size songbirds are somewhat scarce.

56. MYRTLE WARBLER

c. 1925-1944
H. 3⅜. W. 5
Heritage Plantation Collection (1970.5.3)

The painted holly leaves on the base of this ornamental are unusual and probably indicate that it was a special order or a present. The legs are typically ungainly. The rectangular impression is on the bottom. The eyes on this bird are brass tacks instead of the usually encountered painted eyes.

57. DOWNY WOODPECKER DOORKNOCKER

c. 1928-1935
H. 3½. W. 6½
Heritage Plantation Collection (1970.5.2)

This bears the unmistakable hand of the Crowell shop although it is unsigned. The painted tack eyes often relate to an early date as does the carefully painted feather details. A Mr. Fred Bushnell of Brookline, Mass. ordered a "Woodpecker on doorknocker" between 1928 and 1933 and is recorded in the order book.

58. HUMMINGBIRD

c. 1920-1940
H. ¾. L. 4½
Courtesy Donald B. Howes

This life size hummingbird is mounted on the original wire with a wooden dowel on the end. It was made to be stuck in the dirt in a flower pot. Only one or two other examples like this are known, although patterns exist for other sizes which were mounted on the standard bases.

59. CARDINAL
c. 1925-1960
H. 7 L. 7¼
Heritage Plantation Collection (1969.1.2)

This Cardinal is an example of the rather poor workmanship that is sometimes encountered from the Crowell workshop. It appears to have been hastily carved and painted, by all indications, and the result is far from satisfactory. Note the handling of the paint in the area of the beak, for instance. The cardinal was unknown on the Cape until 1957 when it, along with the Tufted Titmouse, appeared from the south. The stained, chip carved base with the rectangular impression indicates that this is probably by Cleon.

60. IMMATURE LITTLE BLUE HERON
c. 1927-30
H. 18¼ W. 15¼
Heritage Plantation Collection (1972.3.8)

The blue bill and dull greenish legs identify this as an immature heron rather than an egret. The pied effect indicates a bird in transition to adulthood. A number of these birds are known on various style bases and at least two photographs of Crowell are known with these in the picture. A pattern in the collection of Shelburne is dated 1927 and is labeled generically, "White Heron"(catalogue number 60). The base is branded with the disintegrated oval brand - another indication that it was made in the late twenties.

61. GREAT BLUE HERON
c. 1925-1930
H. 41¼ W. 36
Heritage Plantation Collection (1969.1.1)

This magnificent heron is branded with the rectangular stamp on the base. An identical carving with different legs and base is in the collection at Shelburne Museum and bears the oval brand and the date 1912. This is probably the same carving mentioned in his 1933 interview in which it is described: " One of the most interesting birds in the collection is the long-legged white heron. The legs are fashioned out of iron to support the heavy body." No other carvings are known with iron legs. These are the largest carvings known to have been made in the Crowell shop. The pattern for this bird is illustrated in catalogue number 20.

62. PAIR GREEN WING TEAL
1940
H. 20 W. 16
Heritage Plantation Collection (1972.3.14 a& b)

The Crowell shop turned out a number of different wall mounts in pairs and singles. These teal are signed in ink "A.E. Crowell/E.Harwich, Mass./Cape Cod/1940" on the male and "Female Green Teal/A.E. Crowell/Maker/Cape Cod" on the other. Both bear the rectangular brand. These wall mounts were made as late as 1955 and one can be seen in the photograph of Cleon (catalogue number 28).

63. WOOD DUCK
c. 1928 -1944
H. 16½ W. 14
Heritage Plantation Collection (1970.5.7)

This Wood Duck is signed "A.E. Crowell" in ink in Elmer's handwriting. The paint and carving are particularly nice on this example.

MINIATURES

Crowell was only twenty when he attempted to carve and paint his first miniature birds. The Canada Goose (cat. number 65) is his earliest dated miniature and displays many of the features that would make the Crowell carvings famous in the years to come. The crossed wing tips and the beginning strokes of the famous paint are readily apparent on this perky goose.

The first "production" miniatures were made just after the turn of the century. They are rather bulky and somewhat naive in appearance, yet display all the essential features that signal the "Crowell look." Again, we find carved wing tips, animated postures and the blended paint. The very first sets were crudely mounted on rough sawn crate boards with chamfered edges or were made as miniature decoys, without bases.

Elmer was quick to refine his technique and the bases became more finished with patterned paint and sanded ends. The final transition, which occurred before 1910, was to mount the miniatures on rounded bases resembling rocks. Minor changes were to occur in coming decades, but the essential form was complete by 1910. The birds made during this period were sleek and well shaped. They grew broader and heavier as the years passed, just as we all do.

FIGURE 61 and 62. Two Goldfinches and two Bluebirds. The examples on the left of each photo were made c. 1910. Those two on the right are from c. 1940-1961. Collections of Steve Tyng and Heritage Plantation.

The first birds were made in groups conforming to the clients' desires. Crowell speaks of an order in 1914 that consisted of 60 miniatures and several of the earliest sets appear to have been made in groups of twelve. A decision was made to make the miniatures in sets of 48 native Cape birds sometime between 1914 and 1926. These were sold to schools, institutions and collectors. Crowell increased the number of miniatures in a set to 75 between 1926 and 1933 consisting of 25 ducks, 25 shorebirds and 25 songbirds. A set of ducks cost $100.00 in 1930 and the songbirds were $75.00. The prices varied somewhat over the ensuing years.

The birds could also be purchased separately. Prices for shorebirds and ducks ranged from $2.00 each in 1927 to $6.00 each in 1933. They were $7.50 by the mid forties and rose to $15.00 by 1959. The ducks and shorebirds generally cost slightly more than the songbirds.

The earliest carvings are generally sleeker and have more realistically defined features than later examples. The birds become decidedly broader during the thirties. They grow even larger during the last decade of the Crowell workshop and pronounced foreheads appear on many of the examples. The bases of the first carvings are often found with colorful painted surfaces and frequently bear one of the ink marks. The paint on the birds was applied in virtually the same manner as was used on decoys. The feather patterns were loose and blended surfaces prevailed. Later, feather patterns were specifically delineated and far more detail was included.

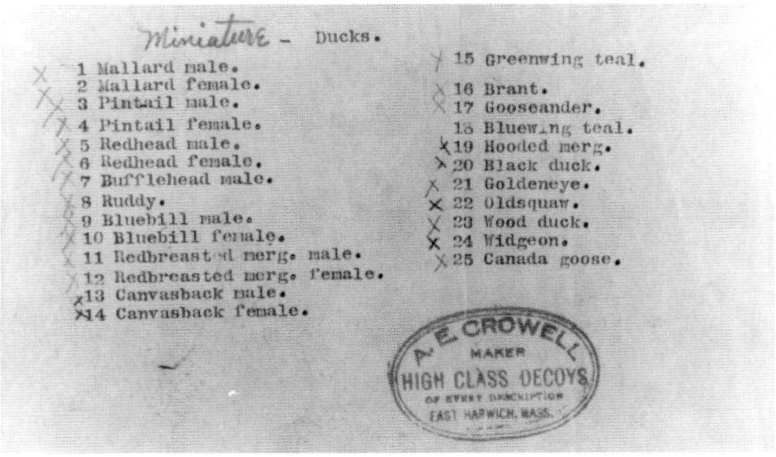

Miniature - Ducks.

1 Mallard male.
2 Mallard female.
3 Pintail male.
4 Pintail female.
5 Redhead male.
6 Redhead female.
7 Bufflehead male.
8 Ruddy.
9 Bluebill male.
10 Bluebill female.
11 Redbreasted merg. male.
12 Redbreasted merg. female.
13 Canvasback male.
14 Canvasback female.

15 Greenwing teal.
16 Brant.
17 Gooseander.
18 Bluewing teal.
19 Hooded merg.
20 Black duck.
21 Goldeneye.
22 Oldsquaw.
23 Wood duck.
24 Widgeon.
25 Canada goose.

A. E. CROWELL
MAKER
HIGH CLASS DECOYS
OF EVERY DESCRIPTION
EAST HARWICH, MASS.

FIGURE 63. List of miniature ducks. Heritage Plantation Collection.

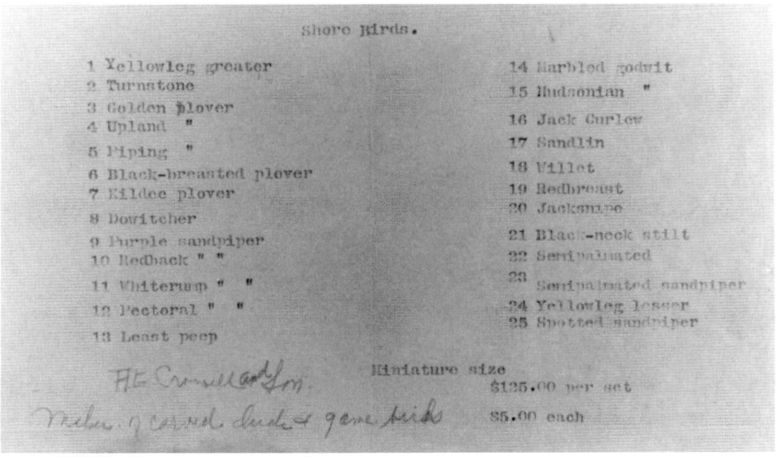

Shore Birds.

1 Yellowleg greater
2 Turnstone
3 Golden plover
4 Upland "
5 Piping "
6 Black-breasted plover
7 Kildee plover
8 Dowitcher
9 Purple sandpiper
10 Redback " "
11 Whiterump " "
12 Pectoral " "
13 Least peep

14 Marbled godwit
15 Hudsonian "
16 Jack Curlew
17 Sandlin
18 Willet
19 Redbreast
20 Jacksnipe
21 Black-neck stilt
22 Semipalmated
23 Semipalmated sandpiper
24 Yellowleg lesser
25 Spotted sandpiper

A. E. Crowell and Son.

Miln. of carved ducks & game birds

Miniature size
$125.00 per set
$5.00 each

FIGURE 64. List of miniature shorebirds. Heritage Plantation Collection.

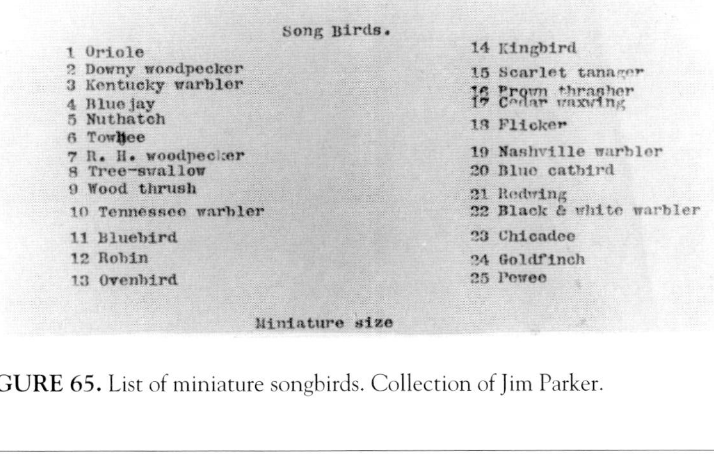

Song Birds.

1 Oriole
2 Downy woodpecker
3 Kentucky warbler
4 Blue jay
5 Nuthatch
6 Towhee
7 R. H. woodpecker
8 Tree-swallow
9 Wood thrush
10 Tennessee warbler
11 Bluebird
12 Robin
13 Ovenbird

14 Kingbird
15 Scarlet tanager
16 Brown thrasher
17 Cedar waxwing
18 Flicker
19 Nashville warbler
20 Blue catbird
21 Redwing
22 Black & white warbler
23 Chicadee
24 Goldfinch
25 Pewee

Miniature size

FIGURE 65. List of miniature songbirds. Collection of Jim Parker.

64. CANADA GOOSE

Joe Lincoln
Accord, Mass.
c. 1890-1920
H. 2¾ L. 5
Courtesy Philip DeNormandie

A great deal of speculation has evolved concerning the possibility that Joe Lincoln (the Accord, Massachusetts decoy maker) influenced the miniature carvings of Elmer Crowell. A typical example of Lincoln's work is presented for comparative purposes. The two men undoubtedly knew each other, but theories concerning who influenced whom will have to remain just that - theories. Significant differences exist between this goose and an early example by Elmer (Figure 65).

65. CANADA GOOSE

1894
H. 2⅜ L. 3⅞
Courtesy The Shelburne Museum,
photograph by Ken Burns.

This goose is signed on the bottom "A.E. Crowell/Maker/1894" in ink. This is printed—unlike other known Crowell signatures; however, there is no doubt that this bird is by his hand. The stance is identical to later, full size decoys and the carved wing tips serve as well as any signature. One can see how the paint evolved from this early stage to the blended process Crowell was soon to use.

66. THREE MINIATURE DUCKS

Elmer Crowell
1901
H. 3 L. 4¼ (Pintail overall)
Courtesy Philip DeNormandie

These three ducks are from a set of twelve, each of which is signed "Elmer Crowell 1st set, 1901" in a contemporary hand. They are from the Dr. Cunningham collection and represent, from left to right: a preening Redhead, a Pintail and a Goldeneye. The crude bases have a simple paint pattern daubed over the surface, yet the ducks have the blended Crowell feathering seen on his earliest decoys.

67. THREE MINIATURE SHOREBIRDS

Elmer Crowell
1901
H. 2⅛ L. 2½ (Dowitcher)
Courtesy Philip DeNormandie

The Golden Plover, Spotted Sandpiper and Dowitcher are from a set of twelve shorebirds made at the same time as the ducks in number 66. The bases are cut from the same crate and have identical markings painted on the top. The detail is remarkable on these lively birds. The striding position of the legs is believed to be unique to this set. Again, the paint is identical to that used on shorebird decoys.

68. SIX MINIATURE SHOREBIRDS

Elmer Crowell
c. 1901-1905
H. 2⅞ L. 8⅛ (overall)
Courtesy Melvin Mirrer

A subtle transformation from the previous examples can be seen with these six shorebirds, part of a set of twelve. The other six are also mounted on a single base. These birds are, from left to right: Ruddy Turnstone, Ringed Plover, Semipalmated Plover, Sandpiper, Golden Plover and Black-bellied Plover. Elmer has begun to slim the bodies of this group and the base has a more sophisticated painted surface of two colors. Notice how he has made the posture of each bird different from one another - a true labor of love.

69. SIX MINIATURE DUCKS (Three in the exhibit)

Elmer Crowell
C. 1901-1905
H. 1½ L. 3
Courtesy The Peabody Museum, photograph by Mark Sexton.

These are actually miniature decoys and are the only examples by Elmer Crowell known to exist other than the goose in figure 65. They are far more refined than the birds in figures 66-68 and probably would date around 1905. The forms and carved details of these birds are vastly superior to the 1901 birds especially when the two Goldeneye Ducks are compared side by side. These ducks were made for Dr. John Phillips and descended in his family until donated to the Peabody Museum.

70. THREE MINIATURE RUDDY TURNSTONES

c. 1901-1930
H. 3 L. 3 (largest)
Courtesy Philip DeNormandie

These three Turnstones graphically illustrate the progression of the earliest Crowell miniatures to those being made three decades later. The example on the right was made for Dr. John Phillips around 1901. It is mounted on wonderful animated striding legs. The second is mounted with straight legs on a rounded base. This style appears to have been made around 1910 for an unknown length of time. Later, the workshop started producing a much more elaborate and detailed version, seen on the left. The feathers are now painted in detail rather than being created in a blended manner.

71. SEAGULL
Elmer Crowell
c. 1901
H. 2⅞ L. 5½
Courtesy Philip DeNormandie

This gull is also from the group of early miniatures owned by
Dr. Cunningham and shares similar features with those birds.
It is especially noteworthy because it shows Crowell was not
limited to carving just miniature ducks and shorebirds at this
early date.

72. GROUP OF EARLY DUCKS Color Illustration PLATE X
c. 1909–1910
H. 3½ L. 4 (Pintail)
Heritage Plantation Collection

These represent some of Crowell's earliest miniatures
mounted on the rounded type base. Family history relates
that these were commissioned in the fall of 1908 and
delivered in 1909 or 1910. They were made for the Robert
Scott family who summered in Osterville. They are all signed
faintly in ink with the "Maker" mark and all have the species
identified on the bottom in Elmer's penciled script.

73. FOUR MALLARD DRAKES

Color Illustration PLATE IX
c. 1910-1960
H. 3¼ L. 5
Courtesy Donald B. Howes, Jackson and Vivian Parker and
Heritage Plantation Collection (1970.2.17)

These four Mallard Ducks represent, from left to right: Elmer
Crowell, 1910, Elmer Crowell, 1942 (see figure 69), Cleon
Crowell, c. 1946-1950 and Cleon Crowell, c.1958. All are
signed or are attributable. The third duck bears the ink
inscription "A.E. Crowell & Son/Harwichport" and the last
duck was purchased directly from Cleon in the late fifties. All
Harwichport addresses indicate carvings by Cleon made after
1945.

The Mallard miniatures were a specialty with Cleon and he
made more of that type than any other. At his best he is
quite the equal to his father's efforts during this period from
1930–1943. The Mallard on the driftwood base is ample
evidence of his talent. These four ducks present a fine
chronology of the miniature carvings and their evolution
over the decades. Note the hump on the head of the last
duck - a feature often present on later birds.

74. PAIR OF MALLARDS

Cleon Crowell
c. 1955
H. 3½ L. 6 (overall)
Courtesy Donald B. Howes

This was purchased directly
from Cleon in the mid-
fifties. It is signed "C.S.
Crowell" in ball point ink
and is stamped with the
"Maker" and oval ink
marks. The double Mallards
were a very popular carving
and sold for $35.00. The
order books reveal that
Cleon sold eight of these
from 1960-1961.

75. THREE WOOD DUCK DRAKES

Color Illustration PLATE IX
Elmer Crowell
c. 1910-1960
H. 3 L. 3⅝
Courtesy Donald B. Howes and Heritage Plantation
Collection (1970.2.1)

This is another group of miniatures which gives a good visual progression of the evolution of the carvings. The example on the left is from the Robert Scott group and dates c. 1910.

The middle duck is signed " "A.E. Crowell/Cape Cod/1941" and the last was purchased from Cleon in the late 1950's. It is signed with the rectangular impression. Note the broad backs and rounded primary feathers on the later carvings.

76. TWO RED-BREASTED MERGANSERS

c. 1910 & 1943
H. 2½ L. 6¼
Courtesy Donald B. Howes and Heritage Plantation
Collection (1970.2.23)

These two examples also illustrate the manner in which the miniature carvings evolved. The later merganser is, again, thicker and broader throughout. It is signed "A.E. Crowell/Cape Cod/1943" and would be one of Elmer's last carvings. It also bears the rectangular impression. Note the close similarity of the paint on the earlier example to that on the full size decoy illustrated in catalogue number 16.

77. TWO GOLDENEYE DRAKES

c.1910-1930
H. 3 L. 4¼
Courtesy Jackson and Vivian Parker and Heritage Plantation Collection (1970.2.7)

These two Goldeneyes exemplify the difficulty in trying to attribute a given carving to either Elmer or Cleon. The very earliest pieces (1900-1912) are often clearly from Elmer's hand and the very latest (1946-1961) are often clearly from Cleon's.

Carvings that fall in between, however, do not appear to have any discernible differences between the two men. Note the similarity of these two Goldeneyes. The one on the left is part of the group made in 1910, therefore, probably by Elmer. The second, which is also quite early, bears the words "Goldeneye" and "Male"in Cleon's distinctive printing. It also has the "MFR" ink stamp.

78. FLYING MALLARD DRAKE

Cleon Crowell
c. 1955
H. 4½ L. 7½
Courtesy Donald B. Howes

This flying Mallard bears the rectangular brand and "CSC" in ink on the reverse. Cleon also made full size wall mounts.

79. TERN

Elmer Crowell
c. 1940-1945
H. 2¼ L. 4¼
Courtesy Donald B. Howes

This could be one of several similar tern species. It is signed on the base "A.E. Crowell/Cape Cod" in the manner of several others in the show which are all dated in the early 1940's.

80. LITTLE TERN

Cleon Crowell
c. 1955
H. 2⅛ L. 5 (overall)
Courtesy Donald B. Howes

The Little Tern is more commonly called the Least Tern. This was made by Cleon and purchased from him during the mid-fifties. It bears the blue paper label on the base. No mention of driftwood bases is noted in the order books before c. 1952.

81. LAUGHING GULL

Cleon Crowell
c. 1955
H. 3 L. 4
Courtesy Donald B. Howes

This also has a blue paper label on the base and is signed in ink "C.S. Crowell". It was purchased from Cleon during the 1950's.

SHOREBIRDS

82. GROUP OF EARLY SHOREBIRDS

Color Illustration PLATE XI
c. 1910
H. 3¼ L. 4½ (Avocet)
Heritage Plantation Collection (1970.3.1-8)

These are part of the miniatures from the Robert Scott family which were delivered around 1910. Note the similarity of the paint on the Yellowlegs to that on a full size decoy of the same period. They are on the bottom row of the color plate.

83. THREE SHOREBIRDS   Color Illustration PLATE IX

c. 1920-1930
H. 5 L. 5½ (Yellowlegs)
Courtesy Philip DeNormandie

All three of these large size miniatures bear the "Makers" ink stamp. The paint, form, size and lack of the rectangular impression indicate that they date from between 1915-1928. The ink mark was not used often after the rectangular impression was made. The impression was much easier to use and did not fade. Note how clear and crisp the painted feathering appears on these superb examples. The Yellowlegs with raised wings is a particularly rare and appealing form. These are the three left hand birds on the top shelf of the color plate.

84. GROUP OF LATE SHOREBIRDS

Color Illustration PLATE IX
c. 1928-1960
H. 4½ L. 5
Heritage Plantation Collection (1972.3.21-29)

These all bear the rectangular stamp and have penciled numbers on the bottom of the bases. These birds are larger overall, as are all later ones, and paint surface shows subtle changes from the earlier group. They also appear somewhat stilted. These include the shorebirds on the second row and the two right hand birds, top row, of the color plate.

SONGBIRDS

85. GROUP OF EARLY SONGBIRDS

Color Illustration PLATE XII
c. 1910
H. 2⅝ L. 3½
Heritage Plantation Collection (1970.4.1-36)

These also are from the group of miniature carvings made for the Robert Scott family around 1909-1910. They are an extraordinary group of meticulously carved and painted birds. Again, as with the others from this group, the paint has been applied in the same manner as found on shorebird decoys of this period.

The detail on these birds and the amount of work to create them is incredible. A rough count of the separate brush strokes needed to mark the feathers on the Chestnut Sided Warbler reveals that Crowell made approximately 350 strokes. All that for just $2.50! These include all the birds on the two lower rows of the color plate.

86. GROUP OF LATE SONGBIRDS

Color Illustration PLATE XII
c. 1928-1960
H. 2¼ L. 3 (Nashville warbler)
Heritage Plantation Collection (1972.3.30-40)

Later carvings have heads that have a pronounced forehead. This is quite noticeable on the Chickadee. These are all signed with the impressed rectangle. The method used to paint the eyes of birds underwent a noticeable change during the 1920's. The earliest method was to make the eyes a simple circle with a dot for the pupil. Later, the eyes were formed by bisecting the circle with black paint. The resulting eyes look like two parentheses. These are illustrated on the top row of the color plate.

87. BLUE JAY

Elmer Crowell
c. 1900-1910
H. 3½ L. 2½
Courtesy The Shelburne Museum, photograph by Ken Burns.

"My first miniature songbird I made and painted/Elmer Crowell/Cape Cod" is written in ink script on the bottom of the base of this wonderful Blue Jay. The painted forget-me-nots are a very special touch. One other identical base is known in a private collection.

88. TWO BLUE JAYS AND TWO

TOWHEES Color Illustration PLATE IX

(Blue Jays)
c. 1909 and 1955
H.3¼ L. 3¾ (largest Blue Jay)
Courtesy Donald B. Howes and Heritage Plantation Collection (1970.4.9)

The jay and the Towhee, on the right, are from the Robert Scott group. The large jay on the left is signed "C.S. Crowell" on the bottom while the Towhee on the left is signed with the rectangular impression. Both date from the 1950's.

FISH CARVINGS

89. MACKEREL
Elmer Crowell
1903
H. 12 W. 27½
Heritage Plantation (1970.5.12)

This is signed on the back of the plaque in ink "A.E. Crowell Maker/E. Harwich/Mass./Cape Cod/1903." This mackerel always hung in Elmer's house over the living room doorway until purchased directly from the family in the late 1960's. The backboard is made of stained pine; other fish are known with mahogany backboards. A pattern for a mackerel with identical measurements is illustrated as catalogue number 157. The signature on the back of the plaque is shown in figure 19.

91. SMALL-MOUTH BASS   Color Illustration PLATE VIII
c. 1925-1960
H. 9 W. 10¾ (Bass) D. 15¼ (plaque)
Courtesy The Cape Cod Five Cents Savings Bank

This leaping fresh water bass is mounted on a round pine board and stamped with the rectangular impression. It has a similar feel to the leaping trout pictured in the c. 1933 photograph of Elmer taken inside the workshop (Figure 22). The Crowells excelled with their fish carvings and were as faithful with the painted surfaces as they were with the birds. This particular example must rank as one of the finest examples of their talents.

90. PICKEREL
c. 1912-1925
H. 9 W. 23½
Courtesy of Mr. Ronald Swanson

This fish is mounted on a mahogany board and bears the oval brand on the back. It matches the pattern illustrated as catalogue number 158. The brass plate is a later addition. The use of mahogany is an unusual, but not unique, feature.

WEATHERVANES

92. CANADA GOOSE WEATHERVANE

c. 1925-1933
H. 14 W. 30½
Heritage Plantation Collection (1970.9.8)

This is not signed in any manner but bears the unmistakable shape and paint patterns used by the Crowells. A number of these goose weathervanes are known in various sizes. This one has painted brass tack eyes. Nina Fletcher Little owns an identical weathervane and relates that a "counterpart had been purchased by a neighbor directly from Mr. Crowell himself in the 1920's." She also relates that he only made seven or eight of these. (p.176. Little By Little) The order books for the years 1927-1933 show that five of these were sold during those years for $35.00 each.

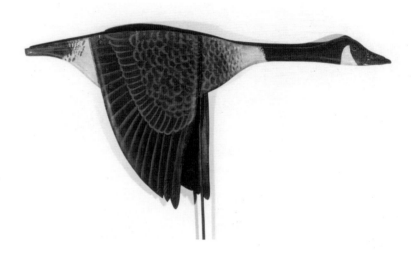

93. YELLOWLEGS WEATHERVANE

c. 1925-1945
H. 3½ W. 16
Heritage Plantation Collection (1970.9.7)

The paint on this bird is more stylized than on the ornamentals. It has brass tack eyes and is branded with the rectangular stamp. Very few of this style were made.

PAINTINGS

94. FATHERS FAVORITES
Elmer Crowell
C. 1877-1880
H. 15¼ W. 20½
Courtesy Philip DeNormandie

This still life of apples is probably the earliest known painting by Elmer . It descended in his family until recent years and may be one of two paintings mentioned in his estate in 1952. Crowell received painting lessons in 1877 and it is quite plausible that this was done at that time. Elmer related that his parents paid for the lessons and perhaps this was his gift to them. The stretcher is handmade.

95. THE WADING PLACE BRIDGE
Elmer Crowell
1890
H. 11½ W. 29¼ (sight)
Courtesy The Cape Cod Five Cents Savings Bank

This is the earliest dated painting known to have been done by Elmer Crowell. It is more accomplished than the previous example and displays Crowell's early control and mastery of colors. It is believed that this particular scene was done as a wedding present to his wife, Laura. The scene depicts the buggy of Dr. Charles Burtel Worthing crossing the Wading Place Bridge on the end of Pleasant Bay Cove on the Chatham town line. The man waving in the boat is probably a self portrait of Crowell. Elmer described himself as a mariner at the time of his marriage in 1890.

96. DOG WITH GAME
Elmer Crowell
c. 1945-1951
Oil on board
H. 10 W. 14
Courtesy Philip DeNormandie

Crowell resumed work with oil paints late in life after he stopped carving. Most of the views are of hunting scenes or game and are quite naive in contrast to the oil paintings he did in his early years.

97. OLDHAM POND SHOOTING STAND
Elmer Crowell
1951
Oil on board
H. 9½ W. 11½
Anonymous Loan

This is a painting of the Oldham Pond gunning stand in Pembroke owned by Dr. John C. Phillips. Elmer Crowell and Fred Gardner worked for Phillips running the stand between 1905 and 1910. This painting was a gift to Gardner from Crowell and carries the following inscription on the reverse:

To Fred and Ida

*This is some of my
dabing I think you
will know the place
I was thinking about
Otis has just droped
in and droped on
the count Ida is
washing the windows
with the polka dot
dress Fred just nailed
one in the air
Them were the days
Fred. With all good
wishes to you
Sincerely
A. Elmer Crowell*

Spring 1951

88 years old

A photograph of the gunning stand taken in 1905 can be seen in figures number 15 and 16.

PATTERNS

A tremendous amount of information has been gleaned from the patterns regarding dates, customers, changes in designs and identification of Elmer and Cleon's handwriting. Only a fraction of the approximately one thousand patterns (owned by Heritage Plantation and Shelburne Museum) are illustrated here but they give an idea of the variety and scope of the work done by the two men. Some relate to specific decoys or models in the exhibit and are so noted. Many others have no information on them. Often, the material used for the patterns can be used to make an approximation of the date - some have been cut from calendars, others from political or theater posters. Groups of patterns were often cut from the same material at the same time and can be related to each other.

Those with the finest details and innovative poses appear to be from Elmer's hand and are quite early - from 1914 to 1925. Cleon also made a number of the patterns, many of which are miniatures. Cleon's handwriting is found on many other patterns dating as early as 1919. Whether he or his father actually drew the pattern is a moot point. It does show, however, Cleon's early role in the business. Measurements are given only for those of unusual interest or size. All patterns are from the Heritage Plantation Collection unless otherwise noted.

LIFE SIZE GEESE AND DUCKS

98. PREENING CANADA GOOSE
1917
H. 9½ L. 22½

This is marked on the back "H.V. Long/1917" and is the pattern for the well known preening goose in a western collection. Crowell made a number of carvings for Long including the following goose and a pair of Dovekie in 1922 (catalogue number 120).

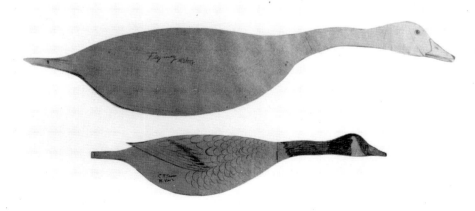

99. TWO CANADA GEESE
c. 1917
H. 7 L. 36 (top goose)

The top pattern was used to make the hissing goose carving shown in the exhibit as catalogue number 50. It was commissioned by Harry Long of Cohasset, Massachusetts. The lower pattern is for a weathervane.

100. CANADA GOOSE HEAD
c. 1917

This appears to have been drawn at the same time as the two geese made for H. V. Long as it is from the same material and is the same general size. The body pattern was not found.

101. BRANT
H. 11 ½ L. 19

The carving to match this Brant has not appeared on the market or in any public collections. It too, appears to have been made in the same general time period as the other life size geese.

102. GREAT BLUE HERON & GREEN HERON
H. 33 L. 27 (Great Blue)

This is the pattern for the Great Blue Heron in the exhibit catalogue number 61. The Green Heron pattern is dated 1930 while the Great Blue is believed to have been made about the same time.

103. WHITE HERON
1927
Courtesy The Shelburne Museum, photo by Ken Burns.

Crowell made several carvings from this pattern. One is displayed in the show and is catalogue number 60. The title page photograph, figure 1, shows Elmer holding another example and the Shelburne Museum has still another in their collection.

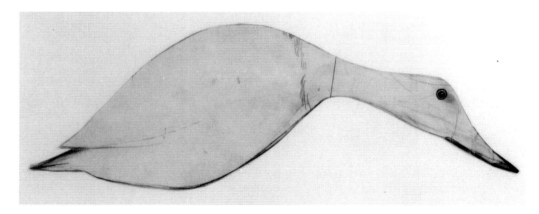

104. CANVASBACK DUCK
H. 5½ L. 17½

No carving is known to match this life-size feeding canvasback.

SHOREBIRDS

105. TWO GOLDEN PLOVERS
1917

107. FOUR SANDPIPERS

These four peeps were cut from the same material at the same time and graphically demonstrate Crowell's predilection for animation in his carvings. These are most likely decoy patterns.

106. FOUR SHOREBIRDS

108. FOUR SANDPIPERS

This is the reverse side of number 107 and shows the cardboard advertising poster Crowell used to make the patterns.

109. WILSON SNIPE (Not in exhibit)

1916
Courtesy The Shelburne Museum, photo by Ken Burns.

An early decoy pattern.

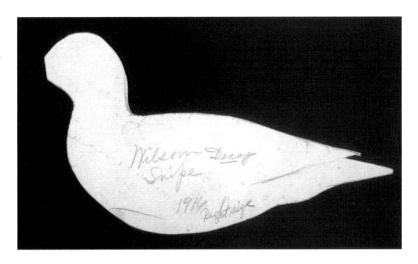

110-112. BLACK-BELLIED PLOVERS

1917-1922

The patterns were revised often to reflect new styles. The six beetle-heads shown here are all different with various size necks, tails and poses. Most are decoy patterns.

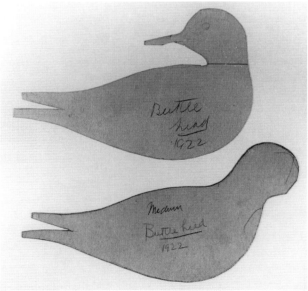

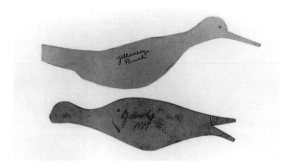

113-115. SEVEN SHOREBIRDS
1915-1925

Six of these are Yellowlegs patterns, each showing different positions or shapes. The Wilson Snipe was made for Dr. Phillips.

116-119.SHOREBIRDS
1914-1935

A variety of birds are illustrated here with the earliest dating from 1914.

120. THREE SHOREBIRDS AND A DOVEKIE
1920-1930

Elmer made a pair of Dovekie, or seadove, for Harry Long in 1922. The Yellowlegs with "wing up" is a smaller version than the one in the exhibit. (catalogue number 35)

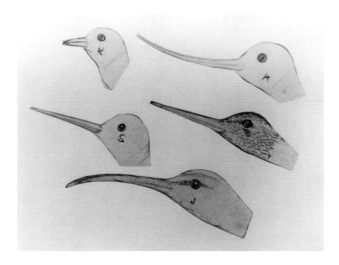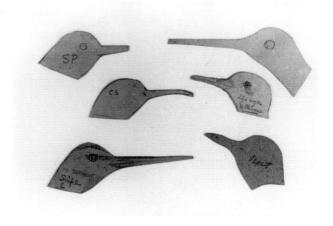

121-122. SHOREBIRD HEADS

DUCK HEADS

123. TWO RED BREASTED MERGANSER HEADS
1914

These are both cut from thin mahogany boards, probably a cigar box.

124. THREE BLACK DUCK HEADS

The top head is a preener similar to catalogue number 44. The bottom may have been made for a hat hanger or as an ornament for placement over a hunting camp door. The Storrow camp was located on the north shore of Pleasant Lake on Cape Cod.

125. REDHEAD

Oldham was the gunning camp of Dr. Phillips in Pembroke. Crowell worked there around 1905-1910.

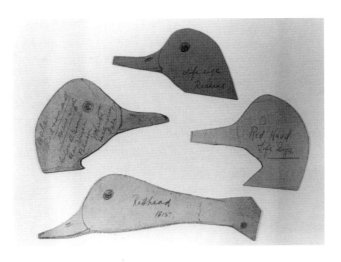

126-127. EIGHT REDHEADS
1915-1930

Shapes and sizes varied considerably over the years. The pattern on the far right, number 126, bears Cleon's handwriting and the one on the left has the paint instructions in Elmer's script.

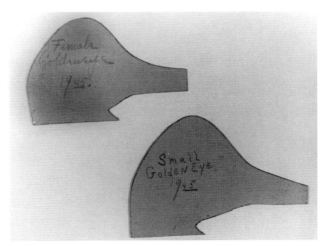

128-130. DUCK HEADS

The two Goldeneye patterns were made by Cleon.

131. THREE BLACK DUCKS

The bottom pattern is a sleeper, the next, a contented duck and the top is a preener.

132. THREE HEADS
1924-1930

The goose head was a pattern for a "fancy hat hanger" for J.J. Storrow in 1924 (see cat. number 48), while the two duck heads were probably used as over-the-door ornaments in his camp. The Green Wing Teal pattern was used to make the carving in catalogue number 47. All three are identified on the back in Elmer's handwriting.

133. CANADA GOOSE HEAD

This was the pattern for a pair of oar hangers.

134-135. TWO CANADA GOOSE HEADS

H 9 L. 9½ (Storrow Model)
c. 1928-1929

The "Storrow Model" is a tremendous oversize pattern used to make three dozen heads for the J.J. Storrow hunting camp on Pleasant Lake in 1929. The pattern is by Cleon. These were stave decoys and the order is recorded in the shop books. The other head marked "Wellfleet Pond" is also by Cleon. An order taken in 1928 records a request for "20 Stave geese for Wellfleet Pond."

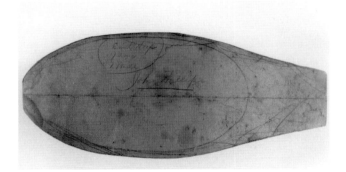

136-139. BODY PATTERNS

The bodies were made by tracing the outline of the overall top view of the bird on a block of wood and then shaping the piece by sight. Some patterns have actual measurements of various distance between anatomical structures, but most do not. Notes on the patterns indicate the hunters or locations the decoys were being made for. One in this group is for Dr. Phillips and another is for the "South Shooting." The workshop sold a large number of decoys to hunters in South Carolina according to the shop records. The "Shelldrake" or merganser pattern, catalogue number 138, is dated 1921 and was made by Cleon. The Canada Goose patterns have a wealth of information on them including the paints to be used. The head and measurements match the decoy in the exhibit (catalogue number 31).

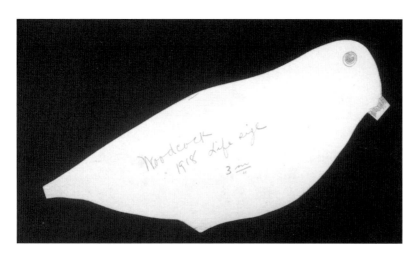

140. WOODCOCK (Not in Exhibit)

1918
Courtesy The Shelburne Museum, Photo by Ken Burns

Upland game birds were more difficult to paint than fowl and consequently cost more. Few examples are known.

141-143. UPLAND GAME PATTERNS

These are all patterns for miniatures except for the group of heads, which are life size. Prices for the carvings are noted on some examples. The pheasant with the base is by Cleon.

MINIATURES

144-145. FIVE MINIATURE WATERFOWL

1917
H. 2½ L. 4½ (goose)

A few of the miniature patterns have great detail and were probably a special order. The Canada Goose pattern is dated 1917.

146-147. MINIATURE WATERFOWL

H. 2 L. 4

These all appear to be part of the same set and all bear script in Elmer's hand.

148. EIGHT MINIATURE DUCKS
1941

Another group of ducks that were a special order and are slightly larger than the earlier miniatures.

149. MINIATURE DUCKS
H. 2½ L. 5¼
1946-1955

These patterns are all by Cleon and are dated after Elmer had stopped working. The "new head" shape can be clearly seen on some of these.

150. GROUP OF SHOREBIRD MINIATURES

The curlew is priced "$1.50 size" which would indicate that it was made from 1920-1925.

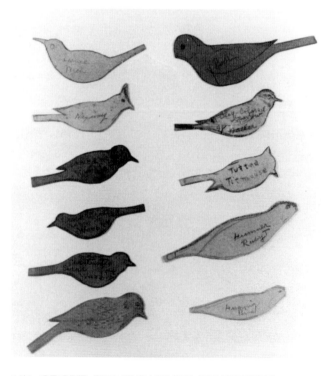

151. GROUP OF MINIATURE SONGBIRDS
H. ½ L. 2¼ (smallest hummingbird)

Two sizes of hummingbirds are in this group along with a Tufted Titmouse - a species that was not seen on the Cape until 1957.

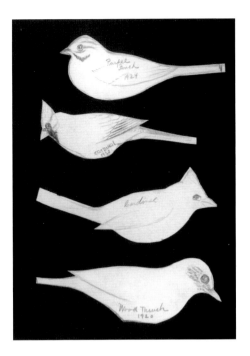

152-154. LIFE SIZE SONGBIRDS (Not in the exhibit)
1920-1937
Courtesy The Shelburne Museum, photos by Ken Burns.

Life size songbirds from the workshop are relatively scarce. It is interesting to note that there are two patterns for a Cardinal - a bird foreign to Cape Cod until 1957. The 1937 oriole pattern is by Cleon.

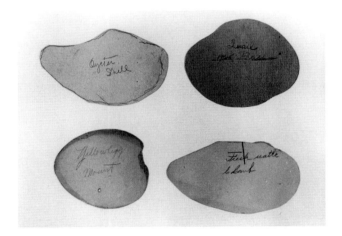

155. TWO PARROTS (Not in the exhibit)
Courtesy The Shelburne Museum, photo by Ken Burns.

No carvings are known that match these two life size parrots. However, a number of other exotic carvings do exist in private collections, including a pelican, a penguin and a tropical fish.

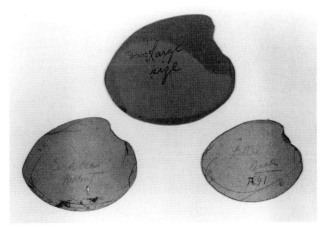

156-157. MOUNTS

These are some of the patterns used for various mounts including the oyster shell (cat. number 37), a fresh water clam and a little neck quahog shell (cat. number 42). The Quail base, dated 1925, bears Cleon's handwriting.

158. SWORDFISH
H. 9 L. 41½

This weathervane pattern bears Cleon's handwriting.

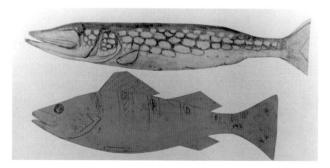

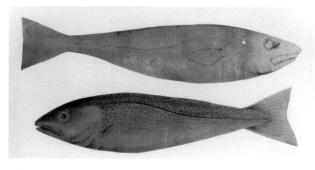

159-162. FISH PATTERNS
H. 5¾ L. 26½ (Haddock)
H. 6¾ L. 18½ (Mackerel)

Most of these fish patterns are life size. The Mackerel and Pickerel match the carvings in the exhibit (catalogue numbers 89 & 90).

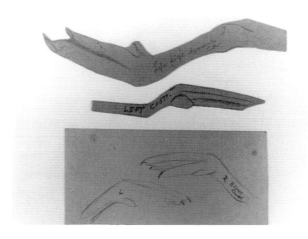

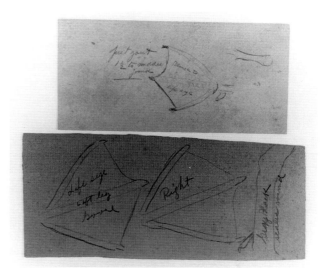

163-166. SKETCHES
1915-1940

These are various sketches, by Elmer, of terns, bird heads and duck and goose feet. The earliest is dated 1915.

167. SHOP SIGN
H. 18 W. 25
Courtesy Philip DeNormandie

This sign hung next to the road in front of the workshop.

168. SIGN
H. 12 W. 26
Heritage Plantation collection

This directional sign was near the intersection of Rte. 137 and Rte. 39.

169. UNFINISHED CARVINGS

These examples show a number of carvings in various stages of completion and are from the workshop. Many have penciled lines for guides to aid in the carving, some have the species identified and one already bears the rectangular impression.

170. ORNITHOLOGY BOOKS
1912-1940
Heritage Plantation Collection

These are some of the ornithology books used by Elmer, and later, Cleon. Two were presented to him by Dr. Phillips and all have Elmer's signature or one of the ink stamps inside. Elmer also used the publications by Edward Forbush for his reference material which were illustrated by Louis Agassiz Fuertes.

171. SHOOTING RECORDS OF WENHAM LAKE
1897-1925
John C. Phillips
Courtesy The Peabody Museum of Salem

172. MANUSCRIPT "WENHAM CAMP SCORE BOOK, 1901"
John C. Phillips
Courtesy The Peabody Museum

This is the original manuscript copy of the shooting records of Wenham Lake kept by Dr. John C. Phillips in 1901. The first line reads: "Crowell arrived. Took a few ducks down." One of Elmer's jobs was the care of the live decoys used at the camp.

173. ORDER BOOKS
1927-1961
Collection of Heritage Plantation

These are some of the records keps by Elmer and Cleon Crowell from 1927 through 1961. They detail the production during those years, give prices, have notations concerning painting methods and even mention orders for glass eyes and the rectangular brand.

174. GUNNING BOX
c. 1875
Mahogany and metal
Courtesy Donald Scothorne

This is an exceptional example of a professional hunter's gunning box. It contains all the necessary tools and materials used in the camp including primers, shot, gun powder, shells, loading tools and duck calls.

175. YELLOWLEGS CALL
Twentieth century
L. 2¾
Courtesy Donald Scothorne

This Yellowlegs whistle was used by Pete Chateau in the early years of this century. He was the Game Warden for the Southeastern district of Massachusetts.

176. SHOTGUN
F. Williams, England
Nineteenth century
Courtesy Ted and Alotta Whitney

This is a typical example of a double-barreled, breech loading shotgun used in the late nineteenth century. Breech loading guns were instrumental to the profession of market gunning. They allowed faster and more accurate shooting than the older muzzle loading guns, and were bemoaned by early conservationists.

177. PUNT GUN
Nineteenth century
L. 55
Courtesy Ted and Alotta Whitney

These large bore guns are often associated with hunting on the Chesapeake Bay; however, they were used on occasion on Cape Cod (One is mentioned on page 48 of "Scientific Duck Shooting in Eastern Waters"). The barrels of these guns could vary in size from a two-inch diameter, weighing nearly 200 hundred pounds, down to two and four gauges. The bore on this example is 1 ⅛ inches. Large bore guns were outlawed by 1918. They were dangerous to use, but a good shot could bag as many as 100 ducks.

178. GUNNING SKIFF
New England
Courtesy The Peabody Museum

This is a typical gunning skiff (sometimes called a "sneak skiff") used to hunt waterfowl. The surface was covered with rushes and grass for camouflage. A similar skiff can be seen in use in figure 11. The boat was propelled by a single sculling oar thrust out the stern and the canvas was pulled over to protect the hunter. This skiff even contained the original jar of hand cream when it was found.

179. MARBLEHEAD DORY
Twentieth century
Courtesy The Peabody Museum

This boat belonged to the gunner and decoy maker, Benjamin Chadwick of Marblehead, Massachusetts. It is typical of the hunting boats used throughout the early twentieth century.

BIBLIOGRAPHY

Barber, Joel, "Wild Fowl Decoys", New York; Dover Publications, 1934, 1954

Connett, Eugene V., Editor, "Duck Shooting", New York; William Morrow & Co., 1947

Delph, Shirley and John, "New England Decoys", Exton, PA: Schiffer Publishing Ltd., ND

Earnest, Adele, "The Art of The Decoy - American Bird Carvings", New York; Clarkson N. Potter, Inc., 1965

Engers, Joe, General Editor, "The Great Book of Wildfowl Decoys", Cynthia Parzych Publishing, 1990

Fleckenstein, Henry A., "Shore Bird Decoys", Exton, PA; Schiffer Publishing Limited, 1980

Frost, Jack, "A Cape Cod Sketch Book", New York; Coward-McCann, Inc., 1939

Hornaday, William T., "Our Vanishing Wildlife", New York; Clark & Fritts, 1913

Kephart, Horace, "Camping", New York; The Macmillan Co., 1917

Lord, Priscilla Sawyer & Daniel Foley, "The Folk Arts and Crafts of New England", New York; Chilton Books, 1965

Mackay, George Henry, "Shooting Journal of George Mackay", Cambridge, MA; The Cosmos Press, 1929

Mackey, William J., "American Bird Decoys", New York; E.P. Dutton & Co., 1965, Republished Bonanza Books

Nye, Russell Scudder, "Scientific Duck Shooting in Eastern Waters", Falmouth, MA; Independent Press, 1895

Phillips, John C., "American Waterfowl", Boston; Houghton Mifflin Co., 1930

Phillips, John C., Editor, "Classics of the American Shooting Field", Boston; Houghton Mifflin Co., 1930

Phillips, John C., "Shooting Stands of Eastern Massachusetts", Cambridge, MA; The Riverside Press, 1929

Phillips, John C., "A Sportsman's Scrapbook", Boston; Houghton Mifflin Co., 1928

Phillips, John C., "A Sportsman's Second Scrapbook", Boston; Houghton Mifflin Co., 1933

Phillips, John C., "Wenham Lake Shooting Record and the Farm Bag", Privately printed, 1926

Sears, Hamblen, "Fur & Feather Tales", New York; Harper & Brothers, 1899

Starr, George Ross Jr., "Decoys of The Atlantic Flyway", New York; Winchester Press, 1974